first edition
scarce
esp. w/ jacket
(wear noted)

Skrallan and the Pirates

WRITTEN BY ASTRID LINDGREN
ILLUSTRATED BY SVEN-ERIC DELER AND STIG HALLGREN

TRANSLATED BY ALBERT READ AND CHRISTINE SAPIEHA

DOUBLEDAY & COMPANY, INC., GARDEN CITY, NEW YORK

SKRÅLLAN OCH SJÖRÖVARNA © 1967 Astrid Lindgren and Rabén & Sjögren. Library of Congress Catalog Card Number 69-10758. Printed in Italy. First Edition.

Far out at sea, among a hundred other islands, lies an island called Saltcrow, and on Saltcrow there is an old red house called Carpenter's Cottage. A little girl known as Skrallan lives there, but only in the summer. In winter she lives in town. No one remembers her real name.

Malin is Skrallan's mother: there she is, hanging out the washing. Petter is Skrallan's father and Melker is her grandfather: they are mending the roof. Melker says, "Old houses always leak, but a handy man can easily fix that."

Skrallan is waiting for her grandfather to fall off the roof. "Now," she says hopefully: she doesn't know any better.

Grandfather always falls down if he climbs up anywhere. As soon as he sets foot on the jetty, he falls into the water. Whenever he tries to hammer in a nail, he hits his thumb instead and his howling can be heard all over the island. But Skrallan thinks he's very funny and entertaining.

3

Skrallan has a little uncle called Pelle. Yes, he really is her uncle. It isn't often you see a ten-year-old uncle who uses a ladder to climb in and out of the house, but Uncle Pelle does, and one day, Skrallan is going to try it too.

From his window, Pelle looks right into the setting sun. "That's what I like," he says. "I like to watch the sea storming and roaring, and I like it when it's calm and smooth, as it is now. I like listening to the gulls screaming as they fly over the sea in the morning; then I know, as soon as I wake up, that I'm on Saltcrow."

5

6

Grandfather fell off the roof this time, too—of course. After shouting and grumbling a bit, he sat down on the steps with Skrallan. Skrallan and her grandfather are very good friends and sometimes, when Malin is busy, he looks after her for hours. Then he gets tired, for Skrallan is always running away, and sighs, "I'm too old for this kind of thing."

But now he is saying, "Look, Skrallan, who's that?"

"Woof-Woof," says Skrallan. She is only two and can't say "Bosun" yet. Bosun is the nicest dog in the world and he's as big as a calf.

Nisse Grankvist and his wife Martha keep shop on the island. They don't move to town when autumn comes, but stay on Saltcrow all year round. Every day they go down to the jetty to meet the boat which brings all the supplies they need for their shop. Bosun usually goes down to the jetty too, but today he has something else to do.

"Hello, Bosun!" Nisse calls, "I know who you're looking for."

Sure enough, Bosun has found Tjorven. And who is he? Tjorven is Nisse's and Martha's daughter, a round, cheerful, determined little girl, the boss of Saltcrow Island.

"Bosun is my dog," says Tjorven, "and he's my best friend too. And Pelle and Stina, of course."

And here is Stina. She has a grandfather, Old Soderman, and she lives with him in the summer. She has no dog, but she does have a little lamb she calls Tottie.

Tjorven says, "It's really Soderman's lamb."

"No she's not," Stina retorts. "Tottie's mine."

"Oh, all right, have it your own way. You're as stubborn as an old goat," says Tjorven, and then she whispers in Bosun's ear, "All the same, it *is* Soderman's lamb. But you, *you* are mine."

Besides Bosun, Tjorven has two big sisters called Teddy and Freddy; but she doesn't see them very often because they are nearly always with Pelle's big brothers, Johan and Niklas. Teddy, Freddy, Johan and Niklas have a club. They call themselves the "Saltcrows" and little children aren't allowed to join. The Saltcrows want to be alone when they sail their raft, and when they build cabins in the woods, and when they sit on a rock cooking sausages over a fire. In fact, they always want to be alone.

"That's all right with me," says Tjorven.

"I don't care," says Pelle.

"Nor I," says Stina. "We want to be alone too. So there."

Tjorven and Pelle and Stina play together every day, and sometimes they let Skrallan play, too.

Tjorven's father has a smokehouse where he smokes the herrings that he sells in his shop. The smell of smoked herring spreads all over the island, and when Bosun gets a whiff, he comes trotting up to see if there are any fish left for him.

Sometimes Nisse has a big smoked herring party down on the beach, and then they all sit round, eating as many herrings as they can: Melker and Petter and Malin and Skrallan and Pelle and Johan and Niklas and Stina and Old Soderman and Tjorven and Teddy and Freddy and Nisse and Martha. And Bosun, of course. They all love smoked herring and think that Saltcrow Island is the only place to live.

Once Skrallan got into the smokehouse while Nisse wasn't looking, and he shut the door and went away. She was frightened and began to cry. It's not much fun being locked up in a dark place. But she pushed and banged at the door until it opened and then ran straight to her mother, who said, "Can this chimney sweep really be my little Skrallan?"

And her grandfather said, "This child is a different color every day. Yesterday she stuck her hands into the jam and was red all over, and the day before, she poured milk over herself and was white all over. I wonder what color she will be tomorrow?"

15

Poor Melker soon found out. The very next day he started painting the kitchen: he likes to keep Carpenter's Cottage looking shipshape. But when Skrallan found herself alone in the kitchen, she decided to help with the painting.

Melker howled when he saw what she had done. He was angry with her for a long time, but then he said, "After all, she's only two."

That happened last summer. Now Skrallan is three and much bigger and smarter. She can talk quite a lot, too.

For her third birthday, Skrallan had a party on the jetty. All the children had cakes and lemonade, and Bosun ate lots of meatballs and had a big piece of cake for dessert.

Tjorven says Bosun is the best playmate in the world, and she is right. As soon as the party was over and Tjorven had taken off her best dress—she always feels uncomfortable in it—she ran off shouting, "Come on, Bosun, let's play hide-and-seek!" Bosun was "it," as usual, and Tjorven, Pelle, Skrallan and Stina ran to hide.

Melker saw them, and as he was only carrying water for Malin and felt like a rest, he shouted, "I'm coming. I'll hide too!"

There isn't another grandfather as playful as Melker in the whole of Sweden.

"I've got the best hiding place," he called.

19

Tjorven caught sight of him as he crawled under Old Soderman's boat. "Uncle Melker, guess what?" she yelled. "Soderman's hens lay eggs under that boat. I bet you're lying in scrambled eggs right now!"

Melker looked around. "I'll bet you're right," he said gloomily, and he didn't play hide-and-seek anymore that day.

Tjorven and Stina climbed up onto the roof of a boathouse and lay there until Bosun came and barked at them to tell them that he had found them.

"You can't hide from that dog," said Tjorven. "He's impossible."

"But he can't find me," Skrallan called. "Come and look for me, Bosun! Behind the nets. In the boathouse. You'll see!"

Bosun found Skrallan, and then he found Pelle, who was lying in the grass. Pelle had forgotten he was playing hide-and-seek and was watching a big, green grasshopper. He likes all sorts of things—dogs, cats, wasps, grasshoppers, beetles—and he is very gentle with them.

Afterward, Skrallan tried to seesaw with Bosun, but it didn't work because Bosun weighs two hundred pounds and Skrallan weighs about thirty-seven.

You wouldn't think Melker would want to play games again after rolling in scrambled eggs, would you? But the next day he was at it again.

He announced, "We'll have a play day today. A whole day of nothing but play from morning till night. Everyone needs a play day now and again."

"For lying in scrambled eggs," said Tjorven.

"Exactly," Melker answered.

And so he arranged a sack race with the children. But then he pulled
his own sack over his head and began playing blindman's buff instead.
The children jumped around him in their sacks, laughing so hard that
they nearly fell down whenever Melker chased them.

But Vesterman didn't laugh. He was trudging by with a basket of herring when Melker ran into him, scattering fish in all directions.

"Now I've got you," Melker shouted, thinking he'd caught Pelle. Was Vesterman angry! He's not a bit playful.

"I'm sorry, Vesterman," Melker said when he had got out of his sack. "Forgive me, we were only playing."

"Very funny indeed," Vesterman said and stumped away angrily.

"That Melker is the craziest person on Saltcrow," he said to Stina later.

"And you're an old grump," said Stina.

"Is that so?" said Vesterman. "I'll tell your grandfather what you said."

"I'm sorry, Vesterman, I didn't mean it." It was an awful thing to say, but Stina doesn't like Vesterman much because he is always teasing her.

27

Then Stina went home and put on long trousers and a lifejacket, for Melker had promised them an outing. She also put a lot of other clothes into a hamper.

"Where are you going? To the North Pole?" asked her grandfather, who was mending his nets.

"Oh, no. Only to Dead Man's Bay, but Uncle Melker says we need lots of clothes when we play with him." Then she was silent for a moment. "Grandfather, if old Vesterman comes here, go in and lock the door. And I didn't call him an old grump. He didn't hear what I said." Then she ran off.

Dead Man's Bay is just the place for a play day. It's a strange and beautiful place, full of old grey boathouses, and there's a schooner there that hasn't sailed for years.

They all went in Nisse's motorboat: Melker and Skrallan and Malin and Petter, Pelle and Stina and Tjorven and Martha.

Melker said, "We'll make two teams and play at pirates."

The two gangs of pirates were called the Sharks and the Hawks. Nisse, Tjorven, Stina and Petter were the Sharks. They went on board the *Albertina*. The Hawks were Melker, Malin, Pelle and Skrallan.

Melker said, "Skrallan is a very small Hawk, but a terrible one."

They had their headquarters in an old boathouse.

Poor old Vesterman was on his way to tar a jetty, and just as he was rowing by the *Albertina,* Nisse dumped a whole pail of water over him.

"Oh, dear," said Nisse. "I thought you were Melker; I'm awfully sorry, Vesterman, we were only playing."

"Very funny," Vesterman grumbled. "But I'm not playing with you, and don't you forget it."

But Skrallan didn't understand. While Vesterman was on his knees, tarring the jetty, she climbed up on his back—she was pretending that he was her horse.

"Would you like some oats?" she asked him.

Vesterman almost wept. "My dear Skrallan, I am not a horse. I have never been a horse and I never will be a horse."

"You will be on Saturday," said Skrallan.

Then Vesterman cried, "Malin, come and take her away! Why can't you all leave me alone? I'm *not* playing with you. I'm *not playing!*"

Then guess what Stina did: she climbed up into the *Albertina*'s crow's-nest. "I'm looking to see what the Hawks are doing," she said. But then she couldn't get down. It's much harder to climb down than to climb up.

"Help!" she cried. "Help! I can't get down."

"It's always the same," said Tjorven. "You got up all right."

"What shall I do?" Stina cried.

"Look at the view," said Tjorven.

But then Skrallan's father climbed up and helped Stina down.

"That's the only useful thing he's done all day," said Stina. Petter had been lying on the quarterdeck, sunning himself and taking no interest in piracy at all.

When pirate bands are rivals they must have something to fight over, so Melker got a stone from the beach and said it was the famous Mysak Diamond, and worth a million, at least.

Tjorven took it down to the *Albertina*'s cabin and hid it in a secret place, and at once, the Hawks and the Sharks began fighting as hard as they could.

Pelle found a bright piece of tin in the Hawk's headquarters and used it to reflect sunlight into the Shark's eyes. "I'll dazzle them," he said, "so they won't see when a Hawk sneaks on board."

He reflected the light at Skrallan, too, and she tried to catch it.

"I jump and jump," she cried, "but it jumps faster."

35

Real pirates probably don't fight by squirting water at each other with bicycle pumps, but the Sharks and the Hawks had to fight with whatever they could find. They had no cutlasses or pistols. Pelle found the pump in a boathouse. Then he borrowed Vesterman's boat and rowed over to the *Albertina* and squirted Tjorven right in the face as she leant over the gunwale.

"Ha, Ha!" she cried, "we have a pump too, a great big bilge pump! Come on, Stina, we'll show him!"

Skrallan didn't understand that she was supposed to be a Hawk. She had climbed on board and joined the Sharks, and now she was helping Tjorven and Stina to squirt water at Pelle. Skrallan thought this was the best part of being a pirate.

"Skrallan! You're a traitor! You're supposed to be a Hawk!" he shouted.

"Yes," Skrallan cried, "that's why I'm squirting water at you." Skrallan doesn't understand about fighting a pirate war.

39

Suddenly, Tjorven thought of something. "Stina, we're going to starve to death. The Hawks have all the food."

Malin had made pancakes and sandwiches, and Tjorven had taken bananas, lemonade and chocolate from the shop. Everything was packed in a large hamper, and the Hawks had the hamper.

"But we have the Mysak," Stina said.

"Yes," said Tjorven, "but what is the Mysak compared to a good pancake? Come on, let's sneak up on them and steal the hamper."

They crept ashore as stealthily as they could, but just as Tjorven came around the corner of the Hawk's boathouse, Melker jumped out and took her prisoner.

"Now, my little Shark, your last moment has come," he cried.

"Ha, Ha," Tjorven said. "What are you going to do? Drown me?"

"That's a good idea," said Melker. "I'll throw you into the sea."

"Ha, Ha, you wouldn't dare," said Tjorven.

"Oh, wouldn't I? We'll see about that!" and he threw her into the water. Then Stina came running up.

"Don't you know you shouldn't throw little children into the sea?" she cried.

40   "No, you shouldn't," Melker said, and threw Stina in too.

"Ha! Ha! We can touch bottom here," Stina shouted.

"Yes, I knew that before I threw you in."

"Uncle Melker, you're a blackguard," screamed Tjorven.

"Yes, I know," said Melker.

"But a nice one, of course," Stina added.

But Melker was right when he said they needed lots of clothes.

But what was Pelle doing? There was no lookout on board the *Albertina*, for Petter was lying on the quarterdeck again.

Nisse had fixed it so the Sharks could haul up the gangplank like a drawbridge and stop the Hawks from getting on board. But Pelle took a running jump and scrambled up onto the gangplank. He crept on board and down to the cabin, where he found the Mysak Diamond in its secret hiding place.

Was Tjorven ever angry when she got back to the *Albertina* and found the Mysak gone and the lookout sunbathing on the quarterdeck.

"Do you know what happens to pirates who forget their duty? They have to walk the plank, if you know what that means."

"Ugh!" said Petter. "That sounds dangerous."

"Yes, it is. You can die of it."

"Mercy!" Petter begged. "Have mercy!"

But it was no use begging. Nisse fastened a plank to the gunwale, Tjorven and Stina blindfolded Petter, and he had to walk the plank. He hit the water with a terrible splash.

"Hurrah!" shouted Malin, who was having a piratical swim. She was a Hawk and thought it was a good thing to make a Shark walk the plank, even though he happened to be her husband.

"Silly Father, going swimming with his clothes on," said Skrallan. "Mother doesn't."

But then Skrallan found something very interesting: a barrel full of feathers and down, the kind used to stuff pillows. It was Vesterman's barrel, but Skrallan didn't know that. She turned it upside down. All the feathers fell out and the wind came and blew them over to Vesterman's jetty. They blew around his ears and stuck to the tar.

"Hi, Vesterman," Skrallan called. "Let's pretend it's snowing and almost Christmas!"

"No, we won't," Vesterman roared. "I am not playing, do you hear me, all of you? *I am not playing!*"

Then Skrallan went into Vesterman's boathouse where she found a big basket. She sat down in it and said, "Hey, Vesterman, let's pretend this is a boat and you're a Shark and have to walk the plank."

"No, thank you," said Vesterman. "Try that on your grandfather instead. He's the one who should walk the plank. He's the craziest person on Saltcrow. In fact, I think you're all crazy."

But Skrallan only said "Mm" and played alone, pretending she was in a boat, until the play day was over and it was time to go home.

Teacher Edition

Vocabulary
Poetry VI

A Beka Book® Pensacola, FL 32523-9100
an affiliate of PENSACOLA CHRISTIAN COLLEGE®

Vocabulary, Poetry VI

Third Edition

Author: James A. Chapman

Contents

VOCABULARY

POETRY

To the Teacher

General Information

Vocabulary and Poetry VI is designed to correlate with the English 12 Curriculum published by *A Beka Book*. It contains vocabulary and poetry for the entire year. Several vocabulary exercises will require the use of *Webster's New Dictionary of Synonyms*.

Vocabulary

There are twelve units of twelve words each: one unit for each three-week period. The words taught in this book were selected because they appear in great literature and because they are words that are likely to appear on standardized verbal tests. Mastery of these words will increase the student's chances of scoring high on any verbal tests he may take. The words were checked in *The Living Word Vocabulary* (Chicago: World Book—Childcraft International, 1981) to help assure that the words are at the proper grade level.

Although there are only 144 words in this book that are directly taught, the students have the opportunity of acquainting themselves with at least 1,248 additional words: 1,196 synonyms and antonyms, 52 different words in the Word Analysis exercises, and a number of other words related to the main vocabulary.

Treatment of the Words

The following information is given for each vocabulary word: (1) word division into syllables, (2) pronunciation, (3) part of speech, (4) etymology, (5) definition, (6) sentence example, (7) synonyms, (8) antonyms, and (9) related forms.

Exercises

There are exercises for every unit, and review exercises after units 3, 6, 9, and 12. The exercises thoroughly teach the vocabulary words by presenting them in different situations: in the context of a sentence, in connection with synonyms or antonyms, in the writing of original sentences, in analogies, and in sentences based on discriminated definitions from *Webster's New Dictionary of Synonyms*.

At the beginning of each unit is a Pre-Test, which is excellent for stimulating interest and competition among the students.

Special mention should be made of the Word Analysis exercises which appear in each unit. These exercises provide a way for students to expand their vocabulary far beyond the vocabulary lists in this book. If students learn the prefixes, roots, and suffixes in each unit and learn the process of analyzing words, they can determine without a dictionary the meanings of thousands of new words, many of which are used in business, chemistry, medicine, and technology. Although word analysis does have some difficulties and limitations, its advantages still make the process extremely valuable.

Teaching Procedure

Suggested Schedule

First Day (10–12 minutes)

(1) Have the students do the Pre-Test to create interest in the vocabulary words in the new unit. After they have indicated their choices, give the correct answers and have them write in the space provided below the exercise the number of correct answers they had. Then have them check their rating on the chart below the exercise.

(2) Introduce the vocabulary unit, pointing out the general type of lesson it is (all Greek words, all verbs, words with certain prefixes or suffixes, etc.).

(3) Pronounce the first word; then have the class pronounce the word in unison. Repeat this procedure for the other eleven words.

(4) Read and briefly explain the etymology of each word. Then read the definition to see how closely it compares to the etymology. Explain to the students that sometimes the meaning of a word changes through the years so that the current meaning of a word may be quite different from what the etymology indicates. But more often than not the etymology will be helpful and will add interesting sidelights to the study of vocabulary.

(5) Read or have some students read the sentence examples for all twelve words.
(6) Tell the students to learn vocabulary words 1–4 and their definitions for the next day.

Second day *(3–5 minutes)*
(1) Briefly review words 1–4.
(2) Assign words 5–8 to be learned for the next day.

Third day *(3–5 minutes)*
(1) Briefly review words 5–8.
(2) Assign words 9–12 to be learned for the next day.
(3) Assign exercise A.

Fourth day *(6–8 minutes)*
(1) Briefly review words 9–12.
(2) Check exercise A.

Fifth day *(5 minutes)*
(1) Briefly review words 1–12.
(2) Assign exercise B. Tell students to peruse the synonyms and antonyms of all twelve words and to do the exercise. Tell them not to attempt to memorize the synonyms and antonyms, but to be able to associate them with the vocabulary words. They should look up in a dictionary any words totally unfamiliar to them.

Sixth day *(5 minutes)*
(1) Check vocabulary exercise B.
(2) Tell students to memorize the prefixes, roots, and suffixes in exercise C (1).
(3) Assign exercise C (2).

Seventh day *(5 minutes)*
(1) Review the prefixes, roots, and suffixes in exercise C (1).
(2) Check exercise C (2).
(3) Assign exercise D.
   Note: There are three different exercise D's. When you assign the one that requires the use of *Webster's New Dictionary of Synonyms,* you will need to emphasize that they should read and understand the discussion of the differences in the words before doing the exercise. You may tell them that you will expect them to be able to give reasons for their choices, based on what the *Dictionary of Synonyms* says about words.
   The first time you assign the exercise D that has to do with analogies, you may want to go through with the students the explanation on pages viii–x of how to do analogies.

Eighth day *(5 minutes)*
(1) Check exercise D.
(2) Assign exercise E.

Ninth day *(6–10 minutes)*
(1) Check exercise E.
(2) Review vocabulary definitions and prefixes, roots, and suffixes for the test.
(3) Assign vocabulary test for the next day.

Tenth day *(12–15 minutes)*
   Give the vocabulary test. This test should thoroughly cover the unit of vocabulary words and the prefixes, roots, and suffixes.

Review Lessons

When you approach the end of the nine weeks, plan to allow several extra days (after you have finished the work on the last unit of that period) to review the units that will be covered on the nine-weeks test and to do the review exercises, which follow units 3, 6, 9, and 12.

Since the nine-weeks tests are comprehensive, be sure to include in your review the prefixes, roots, and suffixes that have been studied, along with the vocabulary words. See Testing Procedure below for an explanation of which units the nine-weeks tests cover.

Testing Procedure

Vocabulary is taught and tested during the first two weeks of each three-week period. Vocabulary is not taught during the third week in order to allow the students more time to study for their grammar-literature exam.

Units 3, 6, 9, and 12 are not tested separately, but rather are tested on the cumulative nine-weeks vocabulary test at the end of each quarter. The first-quarter review test covers units 1–3; the second-quarter review test covers units 1–6; the third-quarter review test covers units 7–9; and the fourth-quarter review test covers units 7–12.

Although the vocabulary tests are referred to as *tests,* they actually count as daily grades. The nine-weeks and semester tests count as two or three daily grades.

Methods of Testing

Methods of testing vocabulary might include (1) giving the word for the definition, (2) giving the definition for the word, (3) matching words with definitions or with synonyms and antonyms, (4) supplying omitted words in definitions, (5) matching prefixes, roots, and suffixes with their definitions.

Poetry

Poetry Goals

The purpose of this section is to acquaint students with a wide variety of good poetry through classroom recitation and memorization. These poems have been selected for their beauty of language, literary greatness, and character-building qualities. As students become familiar with good poetry, they are enriched in mind, spirit, and character, and are inspired with noble aspirations.

Introducing the Poem

The teacher's attitude toward the poem will be transferred to the student. For this reason, the poem should be presented with enthusiasm. The following steps will be helpful:

(1) Build anticipation for the poem by giving some background information about the poem and its author.

(2) Discuss the main idea of the poem.

(3) Have the students mark the places to pause and words to emphasize.

(4) Read the poem with correct phrasing and with good expression. Then have the students read the poem with you once or twice. (You may wish to ask someone in your speech department to record the poem on a cassette tape for your use in the classroom.)

(5) Encourage the students to visualize the poem in their minds while they are saying it.

Memorizing the Poem

A few minutes each day should be set aside for saying the poem. The students should read the poem with the teacher (or cassette tape), using correct phrasing and interpretive expression. The students should become less dependent upon the text each day until they can recite the entire poem without referring to the text.

Testing the Poem

Students will appreciate memorizing their poems and work harder at it if they are tested on each poem. There are a variety of testing methods: (1) have them write the poem from memory; (2) have them write part of the poem—first and last stanzas, for example—if it is especially long; (3) have them say the poem orally in front of the class; (4) ask test questions that call for an answer from the poem; or (5) have them fill in omitted words in the poem.

Suggestions for Answering Analogy Questions

1. An analogy question tests your ability to reason. . . . An analogy expresses a similarity between the relationships of things to one another. . . . This relationship is between the meanings and/or the usages of English words and is usually offered as a sentence written in abbreviated form.

    Example:

    MARE : COLT :: COW : CALF

    As a sentence this reads: A mare is related to a colt in the same way as a cow is related to a calf.

2. An analogy question tests your ability to discover the relationships between the first pair of words (the question pair) and then to find the second pair of words (the answer pair) that is MOST similar in their relationship. Remember to look for the BEST answer, not just a good answer.

    | Procedure |
    ---

3. The KEY to answering analogy questions is analyzing the relationship between the question pair of words. If you do a good job working out this relationship, the answer often becomes obvious. Remember, there is most often more than one relationship between two words.

    (a) Analyze the relationships between the question pair.

    (b) Look for the pair of words with a similar relationship.

    (c) If more than one pair of words fit, return to the question pair.

    (d) Refine and expand the relationships in the question pair.

    (e) Eliminate answers that do not appear to be the *best* answer.

    (f) Always return to the question pair for more clarification if you have trouble selecting the best answer. *The key is always in the question pair.*

    Example:

    SLAVERY : FREEDOM ::
    (A) disease : health
    (B) work : play
    (C) in : out
    (D) war : peace
    (E) enemy : friend

Analysis		*Answer*
Opposite.	⟶	All are opposites (return to the question pair).
Negative—positive.	⟶	Eliminate (B) and (C) since they may be either negative or positive depending on the situation (return to the question pair).
Involve people.	⟶	Eliminate (A) since it involves all living things and not just people (return to the question pair).
A state or condition in which people find themselves.	⟶	Eliminate (E) since these are people themselves and not just conditions or states of beings.

The best answer must be (D).

From *GRE Graduate Record Aptitude Test* by the Arco Editorial Board. © 1980 by Arco Publishing, Inc.

Note: Thoroughly analyze the relationships between the question pair *before* you attempt to find the *best* answer. In the above problem if your original analysis had been: A negative condition in which people find themselves: A positive condition in which people find themselves, the answer would then have been obvious.

4. In an analogy, the same sequence of ideas must be found in both pairs of words.

> ### Example:
> AUTHOR : NOVEL ::
> (A) bust : sculptor
> (B) drama : playwright
> (C) composer : song
> (D) poem : poet
> (E) sermon : preacher

Analysis	*Answer*
A person and the thing he creates.	→ All of the answers include a person and the thing he creates. In the question pair the person comes first, and for the answer to be correct the person must be in the same position. This eliminates all answers but (C).

5. In an analogy, the parts of speech must keep the same relationship.

> ### Example:
> ENEMY : BAD ::
> (A) ally : strong
> (B) dictatorship : evil
> (C) foe : dangerously
> (D) Satan : sin
> (E) friend : good

Analysis	*Answer*
Noun and describing adjective.	→ Eliminate (C) (dangerously—adverb) and (D) (sin—noun or verb) (return to the question pair).
Noun and adjective that describe relationship to you.	→ Eliminate (A) (may just as easily be weak) (return to question pair).
An enemy is a person, with bad being an adjective describing your relationship to this person.	→ Eliminate (B) since dictatorship is not a person (dictator is the person).

Answer must be (E).

Note: If the question pair are the same part of speech, the answer pair must also be the same part of speech but not necessarily the same part of speech as the question pair.

> ### Example:
> NOUN : NOUN :: ? : ? (Your answer may be noun : noun; verb : verb; adjective : adjective; etc. It cannot be noun : adjective; verb : adverb; etc.

If the question pair are different parts of speech, the answer pair must be the same parts of speech as the question pair and in the same order as in the question pair.

> ### Example:
> NOUN : ADJECTIVE :: ? : ? (Your answer must be noun : adjective; it cannot be adjective : noun; verb : adverb; etc.)

6. In an analogy, you are concerned with the relationship between pairs of words and not with the individual meanings of words. Do not compare the individual meanings of words in the question pair with individual words in possible answer pairs. In the analogy A : B :: C : D, you are concerned

with the relationship of A : B as a unit and the relationship of C : D as another unit. Do not concern yourself about the meaning of word A as it relates to word C or D.

Example:
CAGE : PARROT ::
(A)   soar : eagle
(B)   bowl : goldfish
(C)   nest : sparrow
(D)   corral : livestock
(E)   imprisoned : lion

Analysis	_Answer_
A home and the animal staying there.	Eliminate (A) and (E) as they are not homes. Also, cage is a noun, soar a verb, and imprisoned an adjective.
A man-made object and the animal kept there.	Eliminate (C); a nest is not man-made.
A man-made object and the specific animal kept there.	Eliminate (D) because livestock is a general term including horses, cattle, etc.
	The answer is (B) even though a bowl and a cage or a parrot and a goldfish have very little in common. It is the relationship between the question pair of words that is important. That relationship is most similar in answer pair (B).

Pronunciation Key

Symbol	Example	Name
ā	āte	long a
ā̊	chā̊otic	half-long a
â	dâre	circumflex a
ă	făt	short a
ȧ	pȧth [a sound between ă and ä but in America often pronounced ă]	single-dot a
ä	fäther	dieresis a
a	*a*bsorb	italic a
ə	ago (ə·gō)	schwa
ch	chin	
du͡	verdu͡re	ligatured d-u
ē	ēven	long e
ê	fêar [a sound between ē and ĭ]	circumflex-long e
e̊	re̊sist	half-long e
ĕ	ĕgg	short e
e	rec*e*nt	italic e
ẽ	pondẽr	tilde e
g	good	
gz	exalt (gz = x)	
hw	what	
ī	īce	long i
ĭ	ĭt	short i
i	clar*i*ty	italic i
j	jog	
ks	perplex (ks = x)	
kw	quart (kw = qu)	
ᴋʜ̲	= ch in German *ach* and Scottish *loch* [With the tongue in position to say (k) as in *keep*, pronounce a strongly aspirated (h).]	ligatured small-capital ᴋʜ
ṅ	boṅ (French) [indicates that the preceding vowel is nasalized]	nasal n

Symbol	Example	Name
ng	song	
ȼ	ȼver	long o
o̊	o̊bey	half-long o
ô	côrd	circumflex o
ộ	sộft [pronounced (ô) or (ŏ)]	circumflex-short o
ŏ	nŏt	short o
o	*o*bscure	italic o
oi	boil	
o͞o	bro͞od	long double o
o͝o	bo͝ok	short double o
ou	out	
ö	(German *schön;* French *feu*) [Round the lips as if to say (ō) and say (ā).]	
sh	shark	
th	thin	voiceless t-h
~~th~~	~~there~~	voiced t-h
tu͡	virtu͡e	ligatured t-u
ū	ūnit	long u
ů	ůnited	half-long u
û	ûrn	circumflex u
ŭ	ŭp	short u
u	foc*u*s	italic u
ü	(German *grün;* French *vue*) [Round the lips as if to say (o͞o) and say (ē).]	
zh	= z in azure	
'	trifle (trī'f'l) [shows that the vowel is not sounded]	apostrophe

b, d, f, h, k, l, m, n, p, r, s, t, v, w, z have their ordinary English sounds.

c is not used to indicate pronunciation

c in conventional spelling has a sound roughly equivalent to **k** or **s**

The bold symbol (′) as in *attest* (*a*·tĕst′) indicates primary stress, or accent; the lighter symbol (′) as in *attestation* (ăt′ĕs·tā′sh*u*n) indicates secondary stress, or accent.

Note: The schwa (ə) is used only for those unaccented vowels that in all styles of cultivated speech have the neutral sound *uh* as in the word *cut*. The schwa is not used for those unaccented vowels which in cultivated speech have a pronunciation ranging from a short vowel sound to the neutral vowel sound; instead of the schwa for these sounds, the more precise symbols *a, e, i, o, u* are used. These italic vowel symbols indicate that something of the original short vowel sound should be retained in the pronunciation.

Tantalize (Word History)

Tantalus was the mythical king of Phrygia who for revealing secrets of Zeus was condemned to everlasting torment in the infernal abyss of Tartarus. There he was compelled to stand in the river of Hades with water up to his chin and branches of luscious fruit over his head. When Tantalus bent forward to slake his thirst, the water receded so that he was never able to get a drink. When he reached up to pluck the fruit, it swung just out of reach. One can easily understand how our word *tantalize* got its meaning. When one is *tantalized,* he is tormented or teased by being shown something exciting, but never being allowed to have it.

PRE-TEST *In each group below, circle the letter of the word that is nearest in meaning to the word at the left. Then check your answers to see how you rate.*

1. **piquant**	(a) stimulating	(b) vapid	(c) bland	(d) strong
2. **chicanery**	(a) candor	(b) charm	(c) deception	(d) banality
3. **heinous**	(a) humane	(b) cowardly	(c) fearsome	(d) outrageous
4. **redoubtable**	(a) virtuous	(b) atrocious	(c) awesome	(d) timid
5. **banal**	(a) original	(b) commonplace	(c) poignant	(d) expressive
6. **plaintive**	(a) meditative	(b) carefree	(c) joyful	(d) sorrowful
7. **trenchant**	(a) immature	(b) keen	(c) feeble	(d) jubilant
8. **fetish**	(a) talisman	(b) fraud	(c) plaint	(d) stratagem
9. **verdant**	(a) pithy	(b) barren	(c) dull	(d) green
10. **puissant**	(a) powerful	(b) noble	(c) impotent	(d) afraid
11. **entrepreneur**	(a) pedestrian	(b) businessman	(c) chicaner	(d) fetishist
12. **pensive**	(a) melancholy	(b) flippant	(c) thoughtful	(d) cheerful

NUMBER CORRECT		RATING ☐ Extraordinary	☐ Excellent	☐ Good
		11–12 correct	9–10 correct	7–8 correct

1

1. banal	4. fetish	7. piquant	10. redoubtable
2. chicanery	5. heinous	8. plaintive	11. trenchant
3. entrepreneur	6. pensive	9. puissant	12. verdant

1. **ba′nal** (bā′nɐl), *adj.* [From Old French *banal* designating things belonging to feudal serfs, hence commonplace, ordinary.]

    Lacking freshness or originality; commonplace, ordinary.

    From the billing he received, we expected to hear a dynamic speaker, but were greeted with a dreary drone of *banal* notions and languid phraseology.

    Synonyms: insipid, vapid, pedestrian, platitudinous

    Antonyms: original, pithy, stimulating, piquing

    Related forms: banally (adv.), banality (n.)

2. **chi·can′er·y** (shǐ·kān′ĕr·ǐ), *n.* [From French *chicanerie* from *chicaner* to quibble, wrangle, quarrel.]

    Trickery especially in legal dealings; the use of subterfuge or trickery in debate.

    Of his *chicanery* one must always be wary: he will use every ruse imaginable to win a case.

    Synonyms: deception, sophistry, beguilement, duplicity, stratagem, fraud

    Antonyms: candor, straightforwardness, sincerity, forthrightness, frankness

    Related forms: chicane (n.), chicane (v.), chicaner (n.)

3. **en′tre·pre·neur′** (än′trĕ·prĕ·nûr′), *n.* [From French *entreprendre* to undertake.]

    One who organizes and manages a business, assuming the risk of profit or loss.

    Successful *entrepreneurs* can often anticipate price changes and capitalize on them.

    Synonyms: businessman, manager, enterpriser, financier, director

4. **fe′tish** (fĕ′tĭsh, fē′tĭsh), *n.* [From French *fetiche,* from Portuguese *feitiço* sorcery, charm, from Latin *factitius* made by art, artificial.]

    An inanimate object thought to have inherent magical powers, and therefore worshiped. (The word was first used for the idols, amulets, and charms worshiped by the savages of the Guinea coast in Africa.)

    Many primitive tribes of Africa and South America carve *fetishes* out of wood to protect themselves from evil spirits.

    Anything irrationally reverenced.

    Mr. Kharmann, our next-door neighbor, makes a *fetish* of washing and waxing his car.

    Synonyms: talisman, charm, amulet, idol

    Related forms: fetishry (n.), fetishism (n.), fetishist (n.), fetishistic (adj.)

5. **hei′nous** (hā′nʊs), *adj.* [From Old French *hainos* full of hatred, from *haine* hatred.]

    Hatefully bad or wicked; abominable.

    Is the murder of unborn babies any less *heinous* than Hitler's slaughter of millions of innocent people?

    Synonyms: outrageous, monstrous, atrocious

    Antonyms: humane, virtuous, noble

    Related forms: heinously (adv.), heinousness (n.)

6. **pen′sive** (pĕn′sĭv), *adj.* [From Old French *penser* to think, from Latin *pensare* to weigh out carefully, ponder.]

    Thinking deeply or seriously, often of sad or melancholy things.

    Sitting on the riverbank staring vacantly into the water, the girl was startled from her *pensive* mood by a sudden splash.

    Synonyms: thoughtful, reflective, contemplative, meditative

    Antonyms: unreflecting, flippant, heedless, carefree

    Related forms: pensively (adv.), pensiveness (n.)

7. **pi′quant** (pē′kᴀnt), *adj.* [From Old French *piquer* to prick, to sting, ultimately from Latin *picus* woodpecker.]

   Pleasantly sharp or pungent of taste; whetting to the appetite.

   The *piquant* blue cheese dressing added zestiness to the spinach salad.

   Stimulating or exciting interest or curiosity.

   A good speaker will have a *piquant* introduction to gain the attention of his audience before broaching his main points.

   Synonyms: tart, spicy, savory, tangy; captivating, titillating, poignant

   Antonyms: bland, flat, insipid; banal, vapid, jejune

   Related forms: piquantly (adv.), piquantness (n.), piquancy (n.)

8. **plain′tive** (plān′tĭv), *adj.* [From Old French *plaintif,* from Latin *plangere* to strike one's breast, lament.]

   Expressing sorrow; mournful.

   The mourning dove was so named for the *plaintive* cooing sound that it makes.

   Synonyms: dolorous, doleful, melancholy, sorrowful, lugubrious, rueful

   Antonyms: joyful, cheerful, jubilant

   Related forms: plaint (n.), plaintively (adv.), plaintiveness (n.)

9. **pu′is•sant** (pū′ĭ•sᴀnt; pŭ•ĭs′′nt; pwĭs′ᴀnt), *adj.* [From French *puissant,* from Latin *posse* to be able.]

   Powerful; mighty.

   When Elisha's servant saw the *puissant* hosts of the Syrians surrounding the city, he was terrified; but Elisha calmed him by saying, "Fear not: for they that be with us are more than they that be with them."

   Synonyms: potent, forceful, strong, overpowering

   Antonyms: powerless, impotent, strengthless

   Related form: puissance (n.)

10. **re•doubt′a•ble** (rĕ•dout′ᴀ•b′l), *adj.* [From Old French *redouter,* from Medieval Latin *redubitare* to fear (literally to doubt back at): *re-* at + *dubitare* to doubt.]

    Formidable; causing fear; commanding respect.

    Under the brilliant generalship of Alexander the Great, the *redoubtable* Macedonian army overthrew the Persians.

    Synonyms: awesome, dreadful, terrible, fearsome, terrifying

    Antonyms: dreading, timid, afraid, cowardly

    Related forms: redoubtableness (n.), redoubted (adj.)

11. **trench′ant** (trĕn′chᴀnt), *adj.* [From Old French *trenchant,* from *trenchier* to cut.]

    Forceful and effective; keen, penetrating.

    John C. Calhoun, whose home state was the first state to secede from the Union, presented *trenchant* arguments in favor of states' rights.

    Synonyms: vigorous, striking, expressive; incisive, cutting, biting

    Antonyms: flat, banal; feeble, dull

    Related forms: trenchancy (n.), trenchantly (adv.)

12. **ver′dant** (vûr′dᴀnt), *adj.* [From Old French *verdeant* to become green, from *verd, vert* green, from Latin *virere* to be green.]

    Green with growing plants or grass; green in color.

    The *verdant* island resembled a giant emerald from our viewpoint in the airplane.

    Unripe in knowledge or judgment; unsophisticated.

    On his first trip to the city, the *verdant* farm boy gazed in awe at all the sights around him.

    Synonyms: verdurous, green, grassy, grass-covered, plant-covered; inexperienced, immature, naive

    Antonyms: barren, waste; sophisticated, knowledgeable

    Related forms: verdantly (adv.), verdancy (n.)

3

EXERCISE A *From the list of vocabulary words in this unit, choose the one that best completes each of the following sentences. Write the word in the blank provided.*

1. In Ghana, West Africa, pregnant natives carry a fertility _____fetish_____ on their backs, believing that such a practice will cause them to have beautiful children.

2. The influx of tourists provided increased opportunities for the small-town _____entrepreneur_____ .

3. She could not help becoming _____pensive_____ as she watched the plane fading away in the distance.

4. Reporters will resort to any kind of _____chicanery_____ to gain entrance to special events and assume strategic positions.

5. The plot of the novel was _____banal_____; the language, trite; the characters, nondescript.

6. I always enjoy reading the _____piquant_____ short stories written by O. Henry.

7. The newly rich couple were so _____verdant_____ that they did not know what a black-tie dinner was.

8. The slave trade was a(n) _____heinous_____ practice; thousands died during passage across the Atlantic because of starvation and disease.

9. Bees and wasps are _____redoubtable_____ insects, especially to those who have allergies.

10. A versatile instrument in proficient hands, the violin can produce light, cheerful tones as well as mellow, _____plaintive_____ ones.

11. J. Gresham Machen was admirably _____trenchant_____ in his defense of supernatural Christianity.

12. In the system of feudalism, a(n) _____puissant_____ lord controlled the lives of his serfs, and to a lesser extent, the lives of his vassals also.

EXERCISE B *For each word in column **A,** select a word from column **B** that is most nearly a **synonym** of that word. Write its letter in the blank provided.*

	A		B
__j__	1. heinous	**a.**	terrible
__g__	2. pensive	**b.**	sincerity
__m__	3. entrepreneur	**c.**	idol
__c__	4. fetish	**d.**	mighty
__d__	5. puissant	**e.**	insipid
__i__	6. trenchant	**f.**	lugubrious
__a__	7. redoubtable	**g.**	contemplative
__n__	8. verdant	**h.**	sophistry
__e__	9. banal	**i.**	incisive
__f__	10. plaintive	**j.**	monstrous
__k__	11. piquant	**k.**	titillating
__h__	12. chicanery	**l.**	cowardly
		m.	enterpriser
		n.	immature

EXERCISE C *Word Analysis.*

1. *Learn the meanings of the following word parts.*

Prefixes:	Roots:	Suffixes:
mis-[1] bad(ly), wrong(ly)	AGON struggle, contest	**-ac, -iac** pertaining to
mis-[2] hater, hatred	CAD, CAS, CID to fall, to befall, to happen	**-er, -yer** one who, that which
trans- (tra-) across	DIC, DICT to say	**-ian** one who
un- not	FER to bear, to carry	**-men** result of
	JUR to swear	
	MORT death	
	OMNI all	
	PEND, PENS to hang, to weigh, to pay	

2. *Using the Word Analyzer (inside the front and back covers), write down the literal meaning of the following words. First, write the meanings of the various parts; next, rearrange the wording of the parts to formulate a good definition. The first one is done for you.*

transferer	trans-	PREFIX	=	**across**
	FER	ROOT	=	**to bear, to carry**
	-er	SUFFIX	=	**one who, that which**
		DEFINITION	=	**one who (or that which) carries across**
antagonist	anti- (ant-)	PREFIX	=	against, opposite
	AGON	ROOT	=	struggle, contest
	-ist	SUFFIX	=	one who
		DEFINITION	=	one who struggles against
mortal	MORT	ROOT	=	death
	-al	SUFFIX	=	like, pertaining to
		DEFINITION	=	pertaining to death

EXERCISE D *For each of the following words, list the antonyms given in this lesson.*

1. banal   original, pithy, stimulating, piquing

2. chicanery   candor, straightforwardness, sincerity, forthrightness, frankness

3. piquant   bland, flat, insipid; banal, vapid, jejune

4. puissant   powerless, impotent, strengthless

5. verdant   barren, waste; sophisticated, knowledgeable

EXERCISE E *Write an original sentence with each of the following words.* Answers will vary.

1. entrepreneur _____

_____

_____

2. fetish _____

_____

_____

3. heinous _____

_____

_____

4. pensive _____

_____

_____

5. redoubtable _____

_____

_____

Everyday Expressions

Gordian Knot

To "cut the Gordian knot" means to dispose of a difficulty in a bold, decisive manner. The term comes from the following legend:

Gordius, a peasant of Phrygia, Asia Minor, became king of his country through the intervention of the gods, who declared that a new king would appear riding in a peasant's cart. The new ruler consecrated the yoke of his team to Jupiter, and fastened the yoke to a beam with a rope of bark so ingeniously tied that no one could loosen the knot.

An oracle declared that whoever would untie this knot would become master of Asia. When Alexander the Great visited the Acropolis at Gordium, in Phrygia, this knot was shown him and the words of the oracle were repeated to him. "I will loosen the knot" said the famous conqueror, as he cut it in two with his sword.

UNIT 2

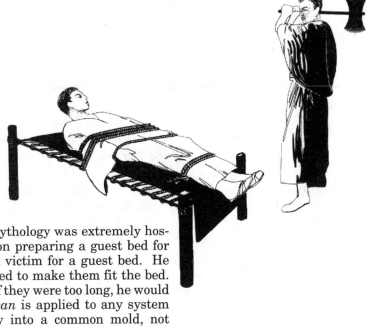

Procrustean (Word History)

The notorious robber Procrustes of Greek mythology was extremely hospitable in his own bizarre way. He insisted on preparing a guest bed for each of his victims, or rather, preparing each victim for a guest bed. He would tie his victims to an iron bed and proceed to make them fit the bed. If they were too short, he would stretch them; if they were too long, he would chop off their legs. Today the term *procrustean* is applied to any system which attempts to force everyone arbitrarily into a common mold, not allowing for individual differences. Socialism, Communism, and the welfare state are all *procrustean* systems.

PRE-TEST *In each group below, circle the letter of the word that is nearest in meaning to the word at the left. Then check your answers to see how you rate.*

1. **exigency**	(a) stipend	(b) tirade	(c) eulogy	(d) emergency
2. **expedient**	(a) appropriate	(b) transient	(c) illustrious	(d) unnecessary
3. **imbibe**	(a) eject	(b) issue	(c) drink	(d) derive
4. **egregious**	(a) fitting	(b) flagrant	(c) notable	(d) daring
5. **incarcerate**	(a) imprison	(b) obliterate	(c) dispel	(d) liberate
6. **inundate**	(a) extricate	(b) ingest	(c) overwhelm	(d) immure
7. **inveterate**	(a) undaunted	(b) irresolute	(c) convenient	(d) established
8. **invective**	(a) praise	(b) remuneration	(c) compensation	(d) abuse
9. **emanate**	(a) terminate	(b) emancipate	(c) originate	(d) extricate
10. **intrepid**	(a) noble	(b) courageous	(c) infamous	(d) cowardly
11. **emolument**	(a) salary	(b) adulation	(c) juncture	(d) commendation
12. **extirpate**	(a) extricate	(b) annihilate	(c) generate	(d) decrease

NUMBER CORRECT ☐   **RATING** ☐ Extraordinary   ☐ Excellent   ☐ Good
                                        11–12 correct   9–10 correct   7–8 correct

1. egregious	4. exigency	7. imbibe	10. inundate
2. emanate	5. expedient	8. incarcerate	11. invective
3. emolument	6. extirpate	9. intrepid	12. inveterate

1. **e•gre′gious** (ė•grē′jŭs), *adj.* [From Latin *egregius* chosen out of a herd: *ex-(e-)* out of + *grex, gregis* herd, literally "towering above the herd."]
   Outstandingly bad.
   > Jesse James, an *egregious* outlaw in the mid-1800s, was ultimately killed by a member of his own gang.

   Synonyms: flagrant, outrageous, notorious, infamous, gross
   Antonyms: illustrious, notable, honorable, noble
   Related forms: egregiously (adv.), egregiousness (n.)

2. **em′a•nate** (ĕm′ə•nāt), *v.* [From Latin *emanare: ex-* out + *manare* to flow.]
   To flow forth or originate from a source.
   > The government of the Union . . . is, emphatically, and truly, a government of the people. In form and in substance it *emanates* from them.   —*John Marshall*

   Synonyms: originate, issue, derive, proceed, arise
   Antonyms: decrease, terminate, stop, cease
   Related forms: emanation (n.), emanative (adj.), emanatively (adv.), emanatory (adj.)

3. **e•mol′u•ment** (ė•mŏl′ū•ment), *n.* [From Latin *emolumentum* profit, advantage, from *emolere* to grind out: *ex-* out + *molere* to grind.]
   Profit or gain arising from employment or position.
   > Christian service is rendered not for earthly *emoluments,* but rather for heavenly reward.

   Synonyms: salary, remuneration, stipend, wages, compensation
   Related form: emolumentary (adj.)

4. **ex′i•gen•cy** (ĕk′sĭ•jen•sĭ), *n.* [From Latin *exigentia* urgency, from *exigere: ex-* out + *agere* to drive.]
   A state of urgency; a situation calling for immediate action.
   > The *exigency* caused by the hurricane was alleviated as thousands of people from neighboring cities helped to feed and shelter those whose homes had been demolished.

   Synonyms: emergency, crisis, juncture, strait, predicament
   Related forms: exigence (n.), exigent (adj., n.)

5. **ex•pe′di•ent** (ĕks•pē′dĭ•ent), *adj.* [From Latin *expedire* literally "to free the feet from fetters," hence to set free: *ex* out of + *pedis* chain for the feet.]
   Necessary or suitable under the circumstances.
   > The Lord Jesus said, "It is *expedient* for you that I go away: for if I go not away, the Comforter will not come unto you; but if I depart, I will send him unto you." —*John 16:7*

   Based on what is to one's advantage, rather than on what is right.
   > Why do we not turn out of office those demagogues who care nothing for what is right, but rather pursue what is *expedient?*

   Synonyms: appropriate, fitting, essential; politic, convenient, opportunistic
   Antonyms: unsuitable, unnecessary, unseemly; detrimental, harmful, inopportune
   Related forms: expedient (n.), expediency (n.), expedience (n.), expediently (adv.), expediential (adj.)

Note: Often, through a process called assimilation, the final consonant of a prefix is changed in order to facilitate pronunciation. For example, **ad**siduous becomes **as**siduous; **in**bibe becomes **im**bibe; **in**peccable becomes **im**peccable. Sometimes the final consonant of a prefix is dropped altogether. For example, *ex-* becomes *e-* before all voiced consonants (b, d, g, j, l, r, etc.): **ex**gregious becomes **e**gregious; **ex**manate becomes **e**manate. (Assimilated forms are listed with the prefixes inside the front cover of this book.)

6. **ex′tir•pate** (ĕk′stĕr•pāt), *v.* [From Latin *extirpare* to root out: *ex-* out + *stirps* root.]

> ***To root out or destroy completely; to exterminate, eradicate.***
>> It is . . . one of the first duties of every government to *extirpate* gangs of thieves. —*Macaulay*

> *Synonyms:* uproot, annihilate, obliterate, demolish
> *Antonyms:* propagate, generate, engender
> *Related forms:* extirpation (n.), extirpative (adj.), extirpator (n.)

7. **im•bibe′** (ĭm•bĭb′), *v.* [From Latin *imbibere: in-* (*im-*) in + *bibere* to drink.]

> ***To drink; to absorb or take in with the senses as if by drinking.***
>> After the drought, the parched ground *imbibed* each precious drop of rainwater.

> *Synonyms:* quaff; absorb, assimilate, ingest, digest
> *Antonyms:* disgorge, eject, exude; dispel, disseminate, teach
> *Related forms:* imbiber (n.), imbibition (n.)

8. **in•car′cer•ate** (ĭn•kär′sĕr•āt), *v.* [From Latin *incarcerare* to imprison: *in-* in + *carcer* prison.]

> ***To imprison.***
>> During the time that he wrote *Pilgrim's Progress,* John Bunyan was *incarcerated* for preaching the gospel against the orders of local magistrates.

> *Synonyms:* jail, impound, confine, immure
> *Antonyms:* free, liberate, release, emancipate
> *Related forms:* incarceration (n.), incarcerator (n.)

9. **in•trep′id** (ĭn•trĕp′ĭd), *adj.* [From Latin *intrepidus: in-* not + *trepidus* alarmed.]

> ***Fearless.***
>> The Special Forces of the United States Army, often called the Green Berets, are *intrepid* men who infiltrate enemy territory to direct and support guerrilla warfare.

> *Synonyms:* courageous, unafraid, undaunted, brave, daring
> *Antonyms:* fearful, scared, cowardly, craven
> *Related forms:* intrepidly (adv.), intrepidness (n.), intrepidity (n.)

10. **in′un•date** (ĭn′ŭn•dāt), *v.* [From Latin *innundare: in-* in + *undare* to flow.]

> ***To cover with water; to overwhelm as if with a flood.***
>> Rising flood waters threatened to *inundate* the small towns along the banks of the Mississippi.

> *Synonyms:* overwhelm, submerge, drown, overpower
> *Antonyms:* uncover, extricate
> *Related forms:* inundation (n.), inundator (n.)

11. **in•vec′tive** (ĭn•vĕk′tĭv), *n.* [From Latin *invectivus* abusive speech, from *invehere: in-* in + *vehere* to carry, thus to assail with words.]

> ***A violent verbal attack; an abusive term.***
>> The speaker's eloquent *invective* against those who do not take the threat of Communism seriously is certainly understandable, because he was tortured for several years in a Communist concentration camp.

> *Synonyms:* abuse, railing, vituperation, tirade, diatribe
> *Antonyms:* praise, eulogy, commendation, adulation
> *Related form:* inveigh (v.)

12. **in•vet′er•ate** (ĭn•vĕt′ĕr•ĭt), *adj.* [From Latin *inveterare* to make or become old: *in-* in, into + *vetus* old.]

> ***Firmly established over a long period; settled in a habit.***
>> Plain clothing and an aversion for anything mechanical are *inveterate* customs of the Amish.

> *Synonyms:* confirmed, chronic, deep-seated, deep-rooted, entrenched, habituated
> *Antonyms:* transient, irresolute, unestablished, unsettled
> *Related forms:* inveteracy (n.), inveterately (adv.), inveterateness (n.)

EXERCISE A *From the list of vocabulary words in this unit, choose the one that best completes each of the following sentences. Write the word in the blank provided.*

1. The _____emolument_____ one receives for his work should be a just indication of how much work he produces.

2. Social ills cannot be _____extirpated_____ so long as the hearts of men remain unregenerate.

3. There shall be appointed . . . such number of . . . justices of peace as the President of the United States shall, from time to time, think _____expedient_____. —*John Marshall*

4. In 1990, Saddam Hussein created a(n) _____exigency_____ in the Middle East when he invaded the tiny oil-rich kingdom of Kuwait.

5. The _____intrepid_____ Simon Bolivar led his ill-equipped army to victory as they pushed the larger, better-trained Spanish forces off the continent of South America.

6. The growing infirmities of age manifest themselves in nothing more strongly than in a(n) _____inveterate_____ dislike of interruption. —*Charles Lamb*

7. Many a student has felt _____inundated_____ with work when he has looked at his course requirements over the whole semester rather than taking matters one day at a time.

8. The _____egregious_____ practice of not reporting a change of marital status to the Social Security Office has resulted in a gross misuse of federal money.

9. During the bloody Reign of Terror of the French Revolution, many nobles and their families were arrested and _____incarcerated_____ before they were tried in courts and guillotined.

10. Patrick Henry's powerful _____invective_____ against the English crown was delivered before the Virginia House of Burgesses.

11. Clara Barton's lobbying for a chapter of the Red Cross to be started in the United States _____emanated_____ from her experiences as a nurse during the Civil War.

12. Our pastor, using as his text Proverbs 20:1, exhorted us not to _____imbibe_____ alcoholic beverages because the Scriptures clearly condemn such a practice and because it contributes to the moral and physical degeneration of society.

EXERCISE B *For each word in column **A**, select a word from column **B** that is most nearly a **synonym** of that word. Write its letter in the blank provided.*

	A	B
d	1. exigency	a. absorb
j	2. incarcerate	b. issue
l	3. egregious	c. submerge
a	4. imbibe	d. crisis
k	5. invective	e. release
h	6. emolument	f. demolish
g	7. intrepid	g. brave
f	8. extirpate	h. wages
i	9. inveterate	i. entrenched
b	10. emanate	j. confine
c	11. inundate	k. tirade
n	12. expedient	l. gross
		m. detrimental
		n. convenient

EXERCISE C *Word Analysis.*

1. *Learn the meanings of the following word parts.*

Prefixes:

ex- (e-, ef-, es-) out (of), away from, without, intensive

***in-*[1]** (il-, im-, ir-) in, into

***in-*[2]** (il-, im-, ir-) not

syn- (sy-, syl-, sym-, sys-) with, together

Roots:

AG, ACT to do, to drive

BIBLI book

CAP, CAPT, CEPT, CIP to take, to seize

CLIN to lean, to slope

FID faith

GEN, GENIT birth, race, kind, cause

PED foot

TRACT to drag, to draw

Suffixes:

***-ent*[1]** one who, that which, -ing

***-ent*[2]** like, pertaining to, -ing

-ment that which; state, quality, act of

-y state, quality, act, result of

2. *Using the Word Analyzer (inside the front and back covers), write down the literal meaning of the following words. First, write the meanings of the various parts; next, rearrange the wording of the parts to formulate a good definition.*

exception

ex-	PREFIX	=	out (of), away from, without, intensive
CEPT	ROOT	=	to take, to seize
-ion	SUFFIX	=	state, quality, act of, -ing
	DEFINITION	=	the act of taking out

homogenize

HOMO	ROOT	=	same
GEN	ROOT	=	birth, race, kind, cause
-ize	SUFFIX	=	to make, to act, to subject to
	DEFINITION	=	to make the same kind

infidelity

in-[2]	PREFIX	=	not
FID(EL)	ROOT	=	faith
-ity	SUFFIX	=	state, quality, act of
	DEFINITION	=	state of not having faith

EXERCISE D *Verbal Analogies. In each of the following questions, a related pair of words or phrases is followed by five lettered pairs of words or phrases. Select the pair that best expresses a relationship similar to that expressed in the original pair. Circle the letter of your answer. [Before you do this exercise, turn to pages x–xii and study the suggestions for answering analogy questions.]*

1. CLASS : STUDENT ::
   (a) citizen : country *A class is*
   (b) cattle : stock *made up of*
   (c) choir : singer *students; a*
   (d) teacher : scholar *choir is made up of singers.*
   (e) church : preacher

2. GLOVE : HAND ::
   (a) foot : shoe *A glove fits on one's hand; a*
   (b) attire : dress *sleeve fits on one's arm.*
   (c) necktie : collar
   (d) sleeve : arm
   (e) apparel : garment

3. EMANATE : TERMINATE::
   (a) predicament : exigency
   (b) obliterate : engender
   (c) imbibe : ingest
   (d) intrepid : scared
   (e) habituated : inveterate
   verb: verb, antonyms

EXERCISE E *Write an original sentence with each of the following words.* Answers will vary.

1. egregious _____

   _____

   _____

2. emolument _____

   _____

   _____

3. expedient _____

   _____

   _____

4. incarcerate _____

   _____

   _____

5. invective _____

   _____

   _____

UNIT 3

Investigate (Word History)

Today when detectives *investigate* a crime they often look first for fingerprints and then for other clues. When the word *investigate* first came into the language, however, its literal meaning was "to follow footprints" (from Latin *in-* "upon" + *vestigare* "to track," from *vestigium* "footprints"). Although the meaning of *investigate* has now broadened to mean "examining something systematically or in detail," the original meaning conveys a concrete image which makes the basic idea of the word easy to remember. The word *vestigium* has also given us the word *vestige*, as, "There were no *vestiges* of liberty left": literally, no footprints or traces of liberty.

Unit 3

PRE-TEST *In each group below, circle the letter of the word that is nearest in meaning to the word at the left. Then check your answers to see how you rate.*

1. **obviate**	(a) improve	(b) permit	(c) meditate	(d) prevent ⊙
2. **penitent**	(a) repentant ⊙	(b) sinful	(c) adamant	(d) infallible
3. **vitiate**	(a) avert	(b) corrupt ⊙	(c) eliminate	(d) elevate
4. **ruminate**	(a) facilitate	(b) invalidate	(c) purify	(d) meditate ⊙
5. **vulnerable**	(a) defenseless ⊙	(b) unconquerable	(c) resolute	(d) unbeatable
6. **impeccable**	(a) fallible	(b) contrite	(c) faultless ⊙	(d) inexorable
7. **pestilent**	(a) harmless	(b) flawless	(c) dangerous ⊙	(d) imperfect
8. **virulent**	(a) raucous	(b) healthful	(c) mild	(d) injurious ⊙
9. **indomitable**	(a) invincible ⊙	(b) acquiescent	(c) conquerable	(d) unprotected
10. **procrastinate**	(a) forestall	(b) hasten	(c) ponder	(d) delay ⊙
11. **strident**	(a) loud ⊙	(b) factious	(c) muted	(d) hostile
12. **insurgent**	(a) remorseful	(b) rebellious ⊙	(c) submissive	(d) obdurate

NUMBER CORRECT ☐   **RATING** ☐ Extraordinary   ☐ Excellent   ☐ Good
 11–12 correct   9–10 correct   7–8 correct

1. impeccable	4. obviate	7. procrastinate	10. virulent
2. indomitable	5. penitent	8. ruminate	11. vitiate
3. insurgent	6. pestilent	9. strident	12. vulnerable

Unit
3

1. im·pec′ca·ble (ĭm·pĕk′ə·b'l), *adj.* [From Latin *impeccabilis* not liable to sin: *in- (im)* not + *peccare* to sin.]

> ***Not capable of sin; faultless.***
>
> Because of his *impeccable* service record, the astronaut was awarded the NASA Distinguished Service Medal.

Synonyms: flawless, errorless, infallible, sinless, undefiled
Antonyms: fallible, culpable, blameworthy, imperfect, sinful
Related forms: impeccability (n.), impeccably (adv.)

2. in·dom′i·ta·ble (ĭn·dŏm′ĭ·tə·b'l), *adj.* [From Latin *indomitabilis*: *in-* not + *domitare* to tame.]

> ***Not easily discouraged or defeated; unconquerable.***
>
> Great Britain's *indomitable* spirit during World War II was due largely to the eloquent and fiery rhetoric of Sir Winston Churchill.

Synonyms: invincible, invulnerable, unbeatable, resolute, determined, irrepressible
Antonyms: conquerable, yielding, submissive, capitulating
Related forms: indomitability (n.), indomitableness (n.), indomitably (adv.)

3. in·sur′gent (ĭn·sûr′jent), *adj.* [Latin *insurgere* to rise up: *in-* in + *surgere* to rise.]

> ***Rising in active revolt against constituted authority.***
>
> Why do you suppose the national press media give so much favorable coverage to the *insurgent* groups in our society?

Synonyms: rebellious, insubordinate, factious
Antonyms: acquiescent, resigned, submissive
Related forms: insurgent (n.), insurgence (n.), insurgency (n.)

4. ob′vi·ate (ŏb′vĭ·āt), *v.* [From Latin *obviare* to hinder, from *ob-* against + *via* way.]

> ***To make unnecessary; to prevent or to do away with.***
>
> Upon this ground, which is evidently the true one, it will not be difficult to *obviate* the objections which have been made. —*The Federalist*

Synonyms: preclude, avert, forestall, ward off; rid, eliminate
Antonyms: effect, facilitate, permit
Related forms: obviable (adj.), obviation (n.), obviator (n.)

5. pen′i·tent (pĕn′*i*·tent), *adj.* [From Latin *paenitens,* from *paenitere* to repent.]

> ***Feeling sorrow for one's sins and being willing to repent.***
>
> The daughter wrote a *penitent* letter to her mother, apologizing for her hasty words.

Synonyms: repentant, contrite, remorseful
Antonyms: obdurate, inexorable, adamant
Related forms: penitent (n.), penitently (adv.), penitence (n.), penitential (adj.)

6. pes′ti·lent (pĕs′ti·lent), *adj.* [From Latin *pestilens,* from *pestis* plague.]

> ***Tending to destroy life; dangerous to the moral, social, or political welfare of society.***
>
> Ungodly men falsely accused the apostle Paul of being "a *pestilent* fellow, and a mover of sedition among all the Jews throughout the world."

Synonyms: detrimental, destructive, ruinous, injurious, baleful
Antonyms: innocuous, harmless, uncorrupting, healthful
Related forms: pestilently (adv.), pestilence (n.), pestilential (adj.)

7. **pro•cras′ti•nate** (prŏ•krăs′tĭ•nāt), *v.* [From Latin *procrastinare* to put forward until tomorrow: *pro-* forward + *crastinus* of tomorrow, from *cras* tomorrow.]

   To put off doing something until a future time; to postpone habitually.

   > The less one has to do, the less time one finds to do it in. One yawns, one *procrastinates*, one can do it when one will, and therefore one seldom does it at all. —*Chesterfield*

   Synonyms: delay, lag, dawdle, loiter
   Antonyms: hasten, hurry
   Related forms: procrastinator (n.), procrastination (n.), procrastinative (adj.), procrastinatory (adj.)

   > *Putting off an easy thing makes it hard, and putting off a hard one makes it impossible.*
   > —*George H. Lorimer*

8. **ru′mi•nate** (rōō′mĭ•nāt), *v.* [From Latin *ruminare* to chew over, from *rumen* throat, gullet.]

   To chew the cud; to meditate or reflect on.

   > He spent many sleepless nights *ruminating* over the perplexing problem and trying to find a solution.

   Synonyms: muse, meditate, ponder
   Related forms: ruminant (n., adj.), rumination (n.), ruminative (adj.), ruminator (n.)

9. **stri′•dent** (strī′dent), *adj.* [From Latin *stridens,* from *stridere* to creak, to make a harsh sound.]

   Loud, harsh, and grating.

   > His bluff, *strident* words struck the note sailors understand. —*Barrie*

   Synonyms: loud, stentorian, earsplitting, hoarse, raucous
   Antonyms: low-pitched, low, soft, muted
   Related forms: stridently (adv.), stridency (n.), stridence (n.), stridor (n.)

10. **vir′u•lent** (vĭr′ū•lent), *adj.* [From Latin *virulentus* poisonous, from *virus* poison.]

    Extremely poisonous, highly injurious; bitterly antagonistic or spiteful.

    > The great obstacle faced by the builders of the Panama Canal was the *virulent* diseases malaria and yellow fever.

    Synonyms: venomous, toxic, lethal; malicious, hostile, rancorous
    Antonyms: harmless, innocuous, mild; gentle, benign, friendly
    Related forms: virulence (n.), virulently (adv.)

11. **vi′ti•ate** (vĭsh′ĭ•āt), *v.* [From Latin *vitiare* to make faulty, corrupt, from *vitium* fault, crime, vice.]

    To weaken morally; to corrupt.

    > Constant exposure to ungodly philosophies can easily *vitiate* one's faith in God's Word.

    To render legally ineffective.

    > The perjury committed by his star witness *vitiated* the attorney's defense.

    Synonyms: debase, deprave, corrupt, pervert, debauch; invalidate, annul, nullify
    Antonyms: elevate, improve, purify; validate, legalize, institute
    Related forms: vitiation (n.), vitiator (n.), vitiable (adj.)

12. **vul′ner•a•ble** (vŭl′nēr•ə•b'l), *adj.* [From Latin *vulnerare* to wound, from *vulnus* wound.]

    Susceptible to wounds; open to attack.

    > We are *vulnerable* both by water and land, without either fleet or army. —*Alexander Hamilton*

    Synonyms: defenseless, exposed, unprotected
    Antonyms: invulnerable, impregnable, unconquerable
    Related forms: vulnerability (n.), vulnerary (adj., n.)

EXERCISE A *From the list of vocabulary words in this unit, choose the one that best completes each of the following sentences. Write the word in the blank provided.*

1. Because Israel failed to drive the inhabitants from the land as God had commanded, they were _____vitiated_____ by the sins of the heathen.

2. Through the death and resurrection of the Lamb of God, the necessity of offering animal sacrifices was _____obviated_____.

3. A deacon must be a man of _____impeccable_____ character and integrity.

4. The _____strident_____ laughter of the insane man echoed eerily down the corridors of the asylum.

5. In 1789, Fletcher Christian and nine _____insurgent_____ sailors proclaimed mutiny on the ship H.M.S. *Bounty*.

6. The _____penitent_____ sinner knelt meekly at the mourners' bench and there met with the God of his youth.

7. In 1796, Edward Jenner discovered vaccination as a means of combating smallpox, a(n) _____virulent_____ disease which had previously been fatal.

8. The _____pestilent_____ philosophy of humanism has permeated American society in the twentieth century, undermining our nation's strong Christian heritage.

9. In medieval times, a primary function of armor was to protect those parts of the knight's body most _____vulnerable_____ to a lance.

10. Martin Luther _____ruminated_____ at length over the opposing concepts of faith and works before embracing the truth of justification by faith alone.

11. When faced with a deadline on a project, she putters around the kitchen, goes shopping with friends, or does anything imaginable to _____procrastinate_____ just a little longer.

12. The Israelites were _____indomitable_____ as long as they obeyed God's commandments; but when they rebelled against God, they were defeated by even their weakest enemies.

EXERCISE B *In each group below, circle the letter of the word that is either a* **synonym** *or an* **antonym** *of the word at the left.*

1. **vitiate** (a) eliminate (b) facilitate (c) meditate (d) purify
2. **pestilent** (a) sinful (b) healthful (c) obdurate (d) culpable
3. **procrastinate** (a) avert (b) forestall (c) ponder (d) dawdle
4. **obviate** (a) eliminate (b) invalidate (c) elevate (d) validate
5. **insurgent** (a) malicious (b) innocuous (c) factious (d) adamant
6. **virulent** (a) mild (b) hoarse (c) inexorable (d) loud
7. **penitent** (a) culpable (b) undefiled (c) resigned (d) contrite
8. **impeccable** (a) adamant (b) blameworthy (c) resolute (d) repentant
9. **ruminate** (a) muse (b) avert (c) annul (d) permit
10. **strident** (a) rebellious (b) muted (c) insubordinate (d) determined
11. **indomitable** (a) submissive (b) flawless (c) defenseless (d) infallible
12. **vulnerable** (a) remorseful (b) irrepressible (c) impregnable (d) inexorable

16

EXERCISE C *Word Analysis.*

1. *Learn the meanings of the following word parts.*

Prefixes:	**Roots:**	**Suffixes:**
hypo- (hyp-) under, below	AM to love	*-able* able to (be)
ob- (oc-, of-, op-) against, toward, completely	CAPIT, CIPIT head	*-ate,*[1] to make, to act, etc. (forms verbs)
	JAC, JECT to throw	
pro- for, before, forward	MOV, MOT, MOB to move	*-ate*[2] having the quality of
super- (sur-) over, above, beyond	PATH feeling, suffering, disease	*-ate*[3] one who, that which
	PROTO first, original, primitive	
	SCI to know	
	VEN, VENT to come	

2. *Using the Word Analyzer (inside the front and back covers), write down the literal meaning of the following words. First, write the meanings of the various parts; next, rearrange the wording of the parts to formulate a good definition.*

superposition

super-	PREFIX	=	over, above, beyond
POS(IT)	ROOT	=	to place, to put
-ion	SUFFIX	=	state, quality, act of, -ing
	DEFINITION	=	act of placing over

omniscient

OMNI	ROOT	=	all
SCI	ROOT	=	to know
-ent[2]	SUFFIX	=	like, pertaining to, -ing
	DEFINITION	=	knowing all

pathological

PATH	ROOT	=	feeling, suffering, disease
-olog(y)	SUFFIX	=	discourse, study
-ical	SUFFIX	=	like, pertaining to
	DEFINITION	=	pertaining to the study of disease

EXERCISE D *Look up the word* invincible *in* Webster's New Dictionary of Synonyms. *Under that word, you will find discriminating explanations for the following words:* invincible, indomitable, *and* impregnable. *After studying these words, decide which of the three words best completes each of the following sentences.*

1. Knowing that it could mean his death, Savonarola displayed ____indomitable____ courage by continuing to preach after he had been forbidden to do so.

2. In 1776, the ____impregnable____ Fort Sullivan withstood the attack of ten British battleships.

3. Because the Philistines held a monopoly on the smelting of iron, their army was ____invincible____ by other nations around them.

EXERCISE E *Write an original sentence with each of the following words.* **Answers will vary.**

1. impeccable _____

   _____

   _____

2. insurgent _____

   _____

   _____

3. obviate _____

   _____

   _____

4. strident _____

   _____

   _____

5. vitiate _____

   _____

   _____

Everyday Expressions

No Man's Land

A "no man's land" is territory that is unclaimed, in which the writ of the king or the state does not run. The phrase is used sometimes figuratively, and is also applied on shipboard to a space amid ships that cannot be regarded as belonging to either the port or the starboard watch; hence, by extension, the phrase is used of a station or a job that is not specifically assigned to anyone.

In American history there have been two regions known as "No Man's Land." One was a strip of public land lying west of the old Indian Territory (now the state of Oklahoma). It was north of Texas, east of New Mexico and south of Kansas. It did not belong to, and was not subject to, any of these states or the territory, and was a refuge for evil-doers from them all. The second "No Man's Land" was a narrow strip of land in Chester County, Pennsylvania, between Maryland and Delaware. Years ago there was considerable dispute over this bit of land, and it led to confusion in the matters of jurisdiction, the paying of taxes, and the like.

In war times, territory lying between the lines of opposing armies and not under the control of either is frequently called "no man's land."

VOCABULARY REVIEW 1
(Units 1–3)

EXERCISE A *In each group below, circle the letter of the word that is most nearly a* **synonym** *of the word at the left.*

1. **emolument**   (a) commendation   (b) compensation   (c) railing   (d) predicament
2. **plaintive**   (a) cheerful   (b) reflective   (c) overpowering   (d) doleful
3. **egregious**   (a) notable   (b) outrageous   (c) polite   (d) detrimental
4. **expedient**   (a) politic   (b) courageous   (c) entrenched   (d) unsuitable
5. **ruminate**   (a) delay   (b) originate   (c) ponder   (d) hurry
6. **puissant**   (a) contemplative   (b) melancholy   (c) potent   (d) detrimental
7. **emanate**   (a) dispel   (b) obliterate   (c) terminate   (d) arise
8. **trenchant**   (a) flat   (b) naive   (c) cutting   (d) terrifying
9. **exigency**   (a) predicament   (b) salary   (c) fraud   (d) eulogy
10. **extirpate**   (a) digest   (b) uproot   (c) confine   (d) propagate
11. **verdant**   (a) knowledgeable   (b) cowardly   (c) inexperienced   (d) resolute
12. **entrepreneur**   (a) idol   (b) extirpator   (c) insurgent   (d) manager
13. **imbibe**   (a) pervert   (b) liberate   (c) assimilate   (d) uncover
14. **redoubtable**   (a) feeble   (b) dreadful   (c) sophisticated   (d) timid
15. **pestilent**   (a) unbeatable   (b) loud   (c) injurious   (d) hostile
16. **vulnerable**   (a) exposed   (b) toxic   (c) unconquerable   (d) insipid
17. **impeccable**   (a) rebellious   (b) sinless   (c) remorseful   (d) blameworthy
18. **vitiate**   (a) avert   (b) improve   (c) impound   (d) debase
19. **fetish**   (a) plaint   (b) ruminant   (c) chicane   (d) charm
20. **indomitable**   (a) conquerable   (b) irrepressible   (c) submissive   (d) adamant

EXERCISE B *In each group below, circle the letter of the word that is most nearly an* **antonym** *of the word at the left.*

1. **piquant**   (a) dreadful   (b) bland   (c) green   (d) tart
2. **intrepid**   (a) courageous   (b) notorious   (c) honorable   (d) fearful
3. **inveterate**   (a) deep-seated   (b) fitting   (c) transient   (d) unsuitable
4. **incarcerate**   (a) teach   (b) liberate   (c) confine   (d) demolish
5. **banal**   (a) atrocious   (b) thoughtful   (c) noble   (d) original
6. **insurgent**   (a) submissive   (b) unbeatable   (c) fallible   (d) captivating
7. **invective**   (a) salary   (b) praise   (c) puissance   (d) remuneration
8. **obviate**   (a) rid   (b) meditate   (c) delay   (d) permit
9. **heinous**   (a) culpable   (b) carefree   (c) humane   (d) melancholy
10. **penitent**   (a) adamant   (b) remorseful   (c) detrimental   (d) soft
11. **chicanery**   (a) straightforwardness   (b) charm   (c) deception   (d) compensation
12. **procrastinate**   (a) elevate   (b) stop   (c) forestall   (d) hasten
13. **inundate**   (a) submerge   (b) cease   (c) digest   (d) uncover
14. **strident**   (a) venomous   (b) low-pitched   (c) healthful   (d) obdurate
15. **pensive**   (a) joyful   (b) forceful   (c) heedless   (d) ruminative

19

EXERCISE C *In each group below, circle the letter of the word that is nearest in meaning to the expression in* **boldface type.**

1. enjoyed the **stimulating to the interest** book review
   (a) banal   (b) piquant   (c) trenchant   (d) verdant

2. the most **extremely poisonous** snake in the serpentarium
   (a) egregious   (b) intrepid   (c) virulent   (d) inveterate

3. built fortifications to make them less **open to attack**
   (a) vulnerable   (b) redoubtable   (c) pestilent   (d) puissant

4. used unnecessary **abusive terms** in his letter
   (a) emoluments   (b) invectives   (c) entrepreneurs   (d) fetishes

5. very difficult to **root out** the weeds
   (a) vitiate   (b) emanate   (c) inundate   (d) extirpate

6. made a **thing irrationally reverenced** of cleanliness
   (a) chicanery   (b) fetish   (c) banality   (d) plaint

7. tends to **weaken morally** our society
   (a) vitiate   (b) obviate   (c) incarcerate   (d) emanate

8. can overcome **firmly established,** sinful habits
   (a) redoubtable   (b) heinous   (c) virulent   (d) inveterate

9. routed by the **not easily discouraged** Sergeant York
   (a) puissant   (b) impeccable   (c) trenchant   (d) indomitable

10. coming with a **powerful** host
    (a) redoubtable   (b) verdant   (c) virulent   (d) puissant

11. sought an advanced degree for the **gain or profits** it would bring
    (a) invectives   (b) ruminations   (c) emoluments   (d) inundations

12. a rashness typical of **unripe in judgment** youth
    (a) strident   (b) verdant   (c) banal   (d) inveterate

13. sheathed his **formidable** sword
    (a) heinous   (b) indomitable   (c) redoubtable   (d) egregious

14. used traveler's checks to **prevent or do away with** the risk of carrying large amounts of cash
    (a) vitiate   (b) inundate   (c) obviate   (d) emanate

15. heard about the **fearless** Jonathan and his armorbearer
    (a) intrepid   (b) insurgent   (c) puissant   (d) strident

16. found it essential to **meditate** on the Word of God
    (a) imbibe   (b) procrastinate   (c) ruminate   (d) obviate

17. blessings **flowing forth** from the hand of God
    (a) emanating   (b) inundating   (c) imbibing   (d) ruminating

18. opposed the **dangerous to our welfare** philosophy of Marxism
    (a) banal   (b) pestilent   (c) verdant   (d) trenchant

19. provides assistance whatever the **state of urgency** of our circumstances
    (a) expedience   (b) virulence   (c) vulnerability   (d) exigency

20. inspired by the **keen, penetrating** analysis of the book of Hebrews
    (a) impeccable   (b) inveterate   (c) piquant   (d) trenchant

EXERCISE D *From the following list of vocabulary words, choose the one that best completes each of the following sentences. Write the word in the blank provided.*

chicanery	imbibe	insurgent	pensive	trenchant
egregious	impeccable	inundate	plaintive	vitiate
expedient	incarcerate	penitent	strident	vulnerable

1. The _____**impeccable**_____ craftsmanship of the diligent shoemaker caused his business to thrive.

2. Jesus said to the _____**penitent**_____ thief on the cross, "Today shalt thou be with me in paradise."

   —*Luke 23:43*

3. Twice every Sunday for years, the _____**trenchant**_____ sermons of Charles Haddon Spurgeon attracted

   an audience of six thousand people to the great Metropolitan Tabernacle in London.

4. The Nile River annually _____**inundates**_____ the Nile Delta, depositing the rich, black soil in which

   high-quality long staple cotton thrives.

5. The _____**strident**_____ screech of rusty door hinges terrified the boys who were exploring the aban-

   doned house.

6. In Paris on July 4, 1789, _____**insurgent**_____ French peasants stormed the gates of the Bastille and

   freed the political prisoners held there.

7. The confession of the defendant was _____**vitiated**_____ because the arresting officer failed to read

   him his rights immediately upon his apprehension.

8. The last major battle of the Revolutionary War was that of Yorktown in which General Washington's

   troops surrounded the British troops, now especially _____**vulnerable**_____ because the British fleet

   could not return in time to help them, and forced their surrender.

9. The President thought it _____**expedient**_____ to remind our fellow-citizens that we were in a state of

   peace. —*Jefferson*

10. Elastic spongin fibers allow a sponge to _____**imbibe**_____ large amounts of water.

11. Because of the _____**egregious**_____ sins of man, God decided to destroy the world with a flood.

12. Oft in the winds is heard a(n) _____**plaintive**_____ sound of melancholy ghosts, that hover round. —*Addison*

13. We got the bride and groom safely away . . . having _____**incarcerated**_____ all the newspaper reporters in

    the little drawing room. —*Sayers*

14. The period of Lord Danby's administration . . . was full of _____**chicanery**_____ and dissimulation on the

    king's side. —*Hallam*

15. Observing her knitted brow and vacant stare, we gathered that she was in a(n) _____**pensive**_____

    mood.

EXERCISE E *In each of the following analogies, a related pair of words or phrases is followed by five lettered pairs of words or phrases. Select the pair that best expresses a relationship similar to that expressed in the original pair. Circle the letter of your answer.*

1. PIQUANT : SPICY ::
   (a) puissant : powerless
   (b) fetish : idol
   (c) banal : banality
   (d) verdant : green
   (e) entrepreneur : director
   (adj : adj; syn.)

2. VITIABLE : VITIATE ::
   (a) repentant : penitence
   (b) infallible : impeccably
   (c) obviable : obviate
   (d) vulnerability : exposed
   (e) procrastinate : dawdle
   (adj : v; rel.)

3. IMBIBE : DISPEL ::
   (a) intrepid : fearful
   (b) emanate : proceed
   (c) salary : stipend
   (d) invective : adulation
   (e) extirpate : generate
   (v : v; ant.)

4. BANAL : PITHY ::
   (a) chicanery : fraud
   (b) plaintive : joyful
   (c) pensively : reflective
   (d) trenchant : incisive
   (e) timid : cowardly
   (adj : adj; ant.)

5. EXIGENCY : CRISIS ::
   (a) emolument : wages
   (b) egregious : noble
   (c) emanate : terminate
   (d) extirpate : demolish
   (e) invective : eulogy
   (n : n; syn.)

6. OBVIATE : AVERT ::
   (a) indomitable : yielding
   (b) repentant : remorseful
   (c) rumination : meditate
   (d) innocuous : pestilent
   (e) vitiator : purify
   (v : v; syn./adj : adj; syn.)

EXERCISE F *Match each prefix, root, or suffix in column **A** with its definition in column **B**. Some definitions may be used more than once.*

	A		B
w	1. trans-	a.	to bear, to carry
z	2. hypo-	b.	for, before, forward
d	3. -ate³	c.	place where, thing which
a	4. FER	d.	one who, that which
s	5. MOV, MOT, MOB	e.	state, quality, act, result of
y	6. FID	f.	to come
r	7. -ac, -iac	g.	all
f	8. VEN, VENT	h.	foot
u	9. CAPIT, CIPIT	i.	able to (be)
b	10. pro-	j.	to use
q	11. ex-	k.	bad(ly), wrong(ly)
k	12. mis-¹	l.	book
v	13. -men	m.	struggle, contest
g	14. OMNI	n.	to know
x	15. CLIN	o.	to swear
i	16. -able	p.	to throw
l	17. BIBLI	q.	out (of), away from, without, intensive
m	18. AGON	r.	pertaining to
t	19. syn-	s.	to move
e	20. -y	t.	with, together
n	21. SCI	u.	head
d	22. -er, -yer	v.	result of
h	23. PED	w.	across
p	24. JAC, JECT	x.	to lean, to slope
o	25. JUR	y.	faith
		z.	under, below

22

EXERCISE G *Word Analysis. The following words contain prefixes, roots, and suffixes that you have memorized. Write down from memory the literal meaning of these words. First, write the meanings of the various parts; next, rearrange the wording of the parts to formulate a good definition.*

extractable

ex-	PREFIX	=	out (of), away from, without, intensive
TRACT	ROOT	=	to drag, to draw
-able	SUFFIX	=	able to (be)
	DEFINITION	=	able to be drawn out of

transferent

trans-	PREFIX	=	across
FER	ROOT	=	to bear, to carry
-ent[1]	SUFFIX	=	one who, that which, -ing
	DEFINITION	=	that which (one who) carries across

promoter

pro-	PREFIX	=	for, before, forward
MOT	ROOT	=	to move
-er	SUFFIX	=	one who, that which
	DEFINITION	=	one who moves forward

sympathy

syn- (sym-)	PREFIX	=	with, together
PATH	ROOT	=	feeling, suffering, disease
-y	SUFFIX	=	state, quality, act, result of
	DEFINITION	=	act of feeling (or suffering) with

supervenient

super-	PREFIX	=	over, above, beyond
VEN(I)	ROOT	=	to come
-ent[1]	SUFFIX	=	one who, that which, -ing
	DEFINITION	=	that which comes beyond (in addition to)

Everyday Expressions

Ear Marked

Anything that is "ear marked" is marked to be set aside for a particular purpose. The reference or allusion is to the practice of marking cattle or sheep on the ear so that they may be recognized readily. The branding of cattle and horses is, of course, a variation of "ear marking."

An old account of the custom says:

"Ear marks and other marks of ownership on cattle, horses, sheep and swine were important, and rigidly regarded where so much value was kept in domestic cattle. These ear marks were registered by the town clerk in the town records and were usually described both in words and in rude drawings."

Sometimes money that is set aside for a particular purpose is said to be "ear marked," although, of course, no especial mark is placed on the money itself or its containers.

UNIT 4

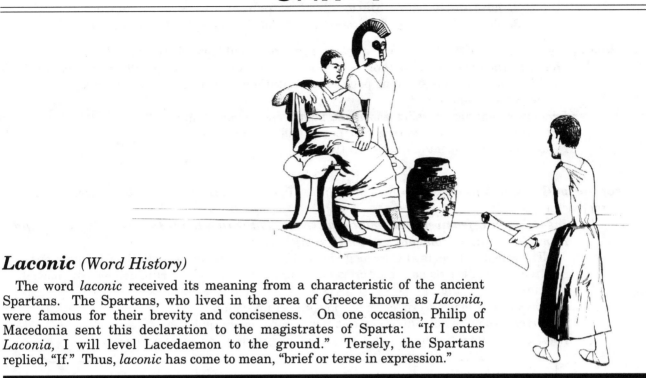

Laconic (Word History)

The word *laconic* received its meaning from a characteristic of the ancient Spartans. The Spartans, who lived in the area of Greece known as *Laconia,* were famous for their brevity and conciseness. On one occasion, Philip of Macedonia sent this declaration to the magistrates of Sparta: "If I enter *Laconia,* I will level Lacedaemon to the ground." Tersely, the Spartans replied, "If." Thus, *laconic* has come to mean, "brief or terse in expression."

Unit 4

PRE-TEST *In each group below, circle the letter of the word that is nearest in meaning to the word at the left. Then check your answers to see how you rate.*

1. **contumely**	(a) self-denial	(b) arrogation	(c) insult	(d) adulation
2. **lapidary**	(a) stonecutter	(b) predecessor	(c) beggarman	(d) harbinger
3. **plagiarism**	(a) child's play	(b) theft	(c) wastefulness	(d) opulence
4. **precursor**	(a) alms-hunter	(b) sinecurist	(c) sanctioner	(d) forerunner
5. **clemency**	(a) severity	(b) mercy	(c) lapidity	(d) mendicity
6. **mendicant**	(a) beggar	(b) herald	(c) frugalist	(d) plagiarist
7. **frugality**	(a) magnanimity	(b) lavishness	(c) thrift	(d) rigidity
8. **penury**	(a) adulation	(b) economy	(c) extravagance	(d) poverty
9. **sanction**	(a) authorization	(b) compliment	(c) condemnation	(d) requiem
10. **dirge**	(a) honor	(b) elegy	(c) respite	(d) obloquy
11. **sinecure**	(a) threnody	(b) plagiary	(c) soft job	(d) applause
12. **hiatus**	(a) pause	(b) mitigation	(c) authorization	(d) vituperation

NUMBER CORRECT ☐   **RATING** ☐ Extraordinary   ☐ Excellent   ☐ Good
                                                     11–12 correct   9–10 correct   7–8 correct

Unit 4 Specific Nouns from Latin

1. clemency	4. frugality	7. mendicant	10. precursor
2. contumely	5. hiatus	8. penury	11. sanction
3. dirge	6. lapidary	9. plagiarism	12. sinecure

1. clem′en•cy (klĕm′en•sĭ), *n.* [From Latin *clementia* calmness, mildness, forbearance.]

Mercy in the exercise of authority or power; leniency toward an offender or enemy.

> *Clemency* . . . is the standing policy of constitutional governments, as severity is of despotism. —*Hallam*

Synonyms: mitigation, relief, easement, beneficence, magnanimity
Antonyms: vengeance, severity, strictness, rigidity, harshness
Related forms: clement (adj.), clemently (adv.)

2. con′tu•me•ly (kŏn′tŭ•me•lĭ; kŏn′tŭ•mē′lĭ; kon•tū′me•lĭ), *n.* [From Latin *contumelia* abuse, insult, reproach.]

Insulting or offensively contemptuous treatment which tends to inflict dishonor and humiliation upon someone; a humiliating insult.

> The religious leaders at the crucifixion of Christ added *contumely* to their ignominious treatment of the Savior: they cried out, "He trusted in God; let Him deliver Him now, if He will have Him."

Synonyms: contempt, scorn, derision, obloquy, vituperation
Antonyms: compliment, adulation, commendation, honor, applause
Related forms: contumelious (adj.), contumeliously (adv.), contumeliousness (n.)

> *It were better to have no opinion of God at all than such an opinion as is unworthy of him; for the one is unbelief, the other is contumely.*
> —*Francis Bacon*

3. dirge (dûrj), *n.* [From Latin *dirige* to direct, from the first word in the Medieval Latin antiphon *Dirige, Domine, Deus meus, in conspectu tuo viam meam,* "Direct, O Lord, my God, my way in Thy sight," adopted from the Vulgate rendering of Psalm 5:8.]

A funeral song or lament; any song or poem expressing mourning.

> Milton's "Lycidas," a *dirge* written in honor of his former fellow collegian Edward King, is sometimes referred to as the greatest short poem in English.

Synonyms: elegy, requiem, threnody
Related forms: dirgeful (adj.), dirgelike (adj.)

4. fru•gal′i•ty (frōō•găl′i•tĭ), *n.* [From Latin *frugalis* pertaining to fruit, profit, utility; thus thrifty, temperate.]

The quality of being thrifty; not spending or using unnecessarily.

> Riches are gotten with industry and kept by *frugality.* —*Hobbes*

Synonyms: thrift, moderation, economy, self-denial
Antonyms: wastefulness, extravagance, prodigality, lavishness
Related forms: frugal (adj.), frugalist (n.), frugalness (n.)

5. hi•a′tus (hī•ā′tus), *n.* [From Latin *hiare* to yawn, gape.]

A break or interruption in something; a gap; a pause.

> Nebuchadnezzar was restored to his kingdom after a humiliating *hiatus* in his reign had taught him that "the Most High ruleth in the kingdom of men, and giveth it to whomsoever He will."

Synonyms: recess, respite, intermission, lacuna, interval
Antonym: continuity, uninterruption

6. **lap′i•dar′y** (lăp′*i*•dĕr′ĭ) [From Latin *lapidarius* stoneworker, from *lapis* stone.]

    n. ***One who works at cutting, polishing or engraving gems.***

        I checked with a *lapidary* to see if the stone I picked up on vacation was of any value.

    adj. ***Pertaining to the art of cutting or engraving precious stones.***

        The king ordered that the person with the greatest *lapidary* skill be found to cut the gems for his new crown.

    Related forms: lapidate (v.), lapidify (v.), lapidator (n.), lapidity (n.)

7. **men′di•cant** (mĕn′di•kant), *n.* [From Latin *mendicare* to beg, from *mendicus* needy.]

    A beggar.

        Not wanting to be thought of as a *mendicant,* the elderly woman refused to accept charity.

    Synonyms: almsman, alms-hunter, beggarman
    Related forms: mendicancy (n.), mendicant (adj.), mendicity (n.)

8. **pen′u•ry** (pĕn′ū•rĭ), *n.* [From Latin *penuria* want, need.]

    Extreme poverty.

        This poor widow hath cast in more than they all: for all these have of their abundance cast in unto the offerings of God: but she of her *penury* hath cast in all the living that she had. —*Luke 21:3–4*

    Synonyms: indigence, want, destitution, privation
    Antonyms: luxury, opulence, affluence, wealth
    Related forms: penurious (adj.), penuriousness (n.)

9. **pla′gi•a•rism** (plā′jĭ•ə•rĭz′m; plā′jə•rĭz′m), *n.* [From Latin *plagiarius* kidnapper; a literary thief, from *plagium* kidnapping, from *plaga* a hunting net.]

    The act of stealing and using the ideas or writings of another as one's own.

        If an author is once detected in borrowing, he will be suspected of *plagiarism* ever after. —*Hazlitt*

    Synonyms: theft, appropriation, arrogation
    Related forms: plagiary (n.), plagiarist (n.), plagiarize (v.), plagiaristic (adj.), plagiarizer (n.)

10. **pre•cur′sor** (prē•kûr′sĕr), *n.* [From Latin *praecursor* forerunner, from *praecurrere: pre- (prae-)* before + *currere* to run.]

    A person or thing that goes before and heralds the coming of another person or thing; one who precedes another in a course or office.

        Kepler more than any [other] man, was the *precursor* of Newton. —*Ellis*

    Synonyms: harbinger, herald, messenger; forerunner, predecessor
    Related forms: precursive (adj.), precursory (n., adj.)

11. **sanc′tion** (săngk′shun), *n.* [From Latin *sanctio* ordain, decree, from *sancire* to hallow.]

    Authoritative permission for an action.

        The pastor's plan to build a new auditorium received the *sanction* of the church board and the warm approval of the other church members.

    Synonyms: ratification, authorization, endorsement, approval
    Antonyms: disapproval, disapprobation, condemnation
    Related forms: sanctioner (n.), sanctionless (adj.)

12. **si′ne•cure** (sī′nĕ•kūr), *n.* [From Latin *sine cura* without a cure, used in Ecclesiastical Latin in the phrase *beneficium sine cura* a benefice (salary) without (the duty of) curing (the souls).]

    A well-paid position with little or no responsibility.

        If all men were under the influence of religion, government would be a *sinecure.* —*Miall*

    Synonyms: soft job, child's play
    Related forms: sinecure (adj.), sinecurism (n.), sinecurist (n.)

EXERCISE A *From the list of vocabulary words in this unit, choose the one that best completes each of the following sentences. Write the word in the blank provided.*

1. Because the young author's work was so much like his own, the well-known author suspected him of __plagiarism__ .

2. Although they had been in the family for over a century, the jewels shone as though they had just come from the wheel of a __lapidary__ .

3. The student learned how to live with great __frugality__ while he was putting himself through four years of college.

4. As elections draw near, some politicians stoop to the use of __contumely__ in an attempt to discredit their opposition.

5. Because his father owned the company, the spoiled young man was given a __sinecure__ , which provided him with a generous salary but required little work.

6. As meekness moderates anger, so __clemency__ moderates punishment. —*Stretch*

7. The missionary had to have the __sanction__ of the government before he could purchase land on which to build a church and school for the natives.

8. A long period of [chemical analysis] . . . was an essential __precursor__ of the present period of synthesis which has been so fruitful of good to mankind. —*Morrison*

9. __Penury__ with love, I will not doubt it, is better far than palaces without it. —*Winthrop Praed*

10. In Egypt one can observe professional __mendicants__ at work, who can at any moment affect a most pitiful aspect when a likely prospect approaches.

11. Walt Whitman's famous poem "When Lilacs Last in the Dooryard Bloom'd" is one of the four __dirges__ which he wrote in memory of Abraham Lincoln.

12. After the execution of Charles I in 1649, the Protectorate of Oliver Cromwell marked a __hiatus__ in the Stuart line; the Restoration of Charles II in 1660 marked the resumption of the monarchy.

EXERCISE B *For each word in column **A**, select a word from column **B** that is most nearly a* **synonym** *of that word. Write its letter in the blank provided.*

	A		B
m	1. hiatus	a.	approval
c	2. mendicant	b.	gem polisher
f	3. dirge	c.	almsman
j	4. plagiarism	d.	harbinger
a	5. sanction	e.	indigence
l	6. contumely	f.	requiem
d	7. precursor	g.	mitigation
b	8. lapidary	h.	strictness
i	9. sinecure	i.	child's play
e	10. penury	j.	arrogation
g	11. clemency	k.	moderation
k	12. frugality	l.	derision
		m.	recess
		n.	rigidity

28

EXERCISE C *Word Analysis.*

1. *Learn the meanings of the following word parts.*

Prefixes:	Roots:	Suffixes:
di- two	BIO life	*-ism* state, quality, act of
non- not	CARN flesh	*-ly*[1] like, having the quality of
pre- before	CUR(R), CURS, COURSE to run, to go	*-ly*[2] in the manner of
se- apart, aside	JUNCT, JUG, JOIN to join, to marry	*-or* one who, that which; state, quality of
	PET, PETIT to seek, to assail	
	PSYCH mind, soul	
	TOM to cut, a section	
	VIV to live	

2. *Using the Word Analyzer, write down the literal meaning of the following words. First, write the meanings of the various parts; next, rearrange the wording of the parts to formulate a good definition.*

psychobiological

PSYCH(O)	ROOT	=	mind, soul
BIO	ROOT	=	life
-log(y)	SUFFIX	=	study, discourse
-ical	SUFFIX	=	like, pertaining to
	DEFINITION	=	pertaining to the study of life and mind

precursor

pre-	PREFIX	=	before
CURS	ROOT	=	to run, to go
-or	SUFFIX	=	one who, that which; state, quality of
	DEFINITION	=	one who (that which) runs (goes) before

carnality

CARN	ROOT	=	flesh
-al	SUFFIX	=	like, pertaining to
-ity	SUFFIX	=	state, quality, act of
	DEFINITION	=	state of pertaining to the flesh

The virtues of enterprise, diligence, and thrift are the indispensable foundation of any complex and vigorous civilization. It was Puritanism which, by investing them with a supernatural sanction, turned them from an unsocial eccentricity into a habit, and a religion.
—*R. H. Tawney*

EXERCISE D *For each of the following words, list the antonyms given in this lesson.*

1. clemency vengeance, severity, strictness, rigidity, harshness

2. contumely compliment, adulation, commendation, honor, applause

3. frugality wastefulness, extravagance, prodigality, lavishness

4. hiatus continuity, uninterruption

5. penury luxury, opulence, affluence, wealth

Units
4

> *Without frugality none can be rich, and with it very few would be poor.* —Samuel Johnson

EXERCISE E *Write an original sentence with each of the following words.* Answers will vary.

1. dirge _____

_____

_____

2. mendicant _____

_____

_____

3. plagiarism _____

_____

_____

4. precursor _____

_____

_____

5. sanction _____

_____

_____

UNIT 5

Malapropism (Word History)

From the French phrase *mal à propos,* meaning "inappropriate," the Irish dramatist Richard Brinsley Sheridan developed the character Mrs. Malaprop for his drama *The Rivals* (1775). Mrs. Malaprop, the aunt of heiress Lydia Languish was noted for her "select words so ingeniously misapplied without being mispronounced" (Sheridan). The following are examples of the ludicrous malapropisms that constantly rolled off the tongue of Mrs. Malaprop: "She's as headstrong as an *allegory* on the banks of the Nile," "I have since laid Sir Anthony's *preposition* before her," "My *affluence* over my niece is very small," "He can tell you the *perpendiculars.*" One can easily understand why a "ridiculous misuse of a word" is now termed a *malapropism.* What word could be more "appropriate"?

PRE-TEST *In each group below, circle the letter of the word that is nearest in meaning to the word at the left. Then check your answers to see how you rate.*

1. **deleterious** (a) acidic (b) healing (c) unremitting (d) injurious
2. **epithet** (a) touchstone (b) nickname (c) norm (d) elixir
3. **panacea** (a) cure-all (b) appellation (c) nuisance (d) delight
4. **plethora** (a) dearth (b) abomination (c) joy (d) excess
5. **agnostic** (a) believer (b) skeptic (c) haranguer (d) rabble-rouser
6. **demagogue** (a) agitator (b) atheist (c) Christian (d) theist
7. **pseudonym** (a) yardstick (b) blessing (c) interdiction (d) pen name
8. **idiosyncrasy** (a) superfluity (b) insufficiency (c) peculiarity (d) profusion
9. **anathema** (a) damnation (b) acceptance (c) nostrum (d) admiration
10. **sporadic** (a) sardonic (b) cordial (c) occasional (d) hurtful
11. **criterion** (a) designation (b) gauge (c) oddity (d) alias
12. **caustic** (a) ruinous (b) beneficial (c) burning (d) infrequent

NUMBER CORRECT ☐ **RATING** ☐ Extraordinary ☐ Excellent ☐ Good
11–12 correct   9–10 correct   7–8 correct

31

1. **agnostic**	4. **criterion**	7. **epithet**	10. **plethora**
2. **anathema**	5. **deleterious**	8. **idiosyncrasy**	11. **pseudonym**
3. **caustic**	6. **demagogue**	9. **panacea**	12. **sporadic**

1. **ag•nos′tic** (ăg•nŏs′tĭk), *n.* [From Greek *agnostos* unknowing, from *a-* not + *gignoskein* to know.]

   One who holds that the existence of God is unknown and unknowable; one who asserts that all claims to knowledge are uncertain.

   In theory, he [Professor Huxley] is a great and even severe *agnostic,* who goes about exhorting all men to know how little they know. —*The Spectator*

   Synonyms: atheist, deist, freethinker, unbeliever, infidel, skeptic
   Antonyms: believer, Christian, theist
   Related forms: agnostically (adv.), agnosticism (n.)

2. **a•nath′e•ma** (ə•năth′ĕ•mə), *n.* [From Greek *anathema* originally "a thing devoted" but in later usage "a thing devoted to evil, an accursed thing," from *anatithenai: ana-* up + *tithenai* to put.]

   A person or thing accursed or consigned to damnation; a formal ecclesiastical curse or ban.

   The apostle Paul wished that he could become *anathema* if only his brethren could be saved.

   Synonyms: damnation, interdiction, excommunication, banishment
   Antonyms: reception, acceptance, sanction, protection

   A person or thing greatly detested.

   As the chairman of the national defense committee, the conservative senator was *anathema* to the liberals.

   Synonyms: abomination, abhorrence, nuisance
   Antonyms: admiration, delight, joy

   A curse or imprecation generally.

   The farmer breathed out *anathemas* on the hordes of crows which were destroying his crops.

   Synonyms: malediction, execration, fulmination, denunciation
   Antonyms: blessing, benediction, praise
   Related forms: anathematize (v.), anathematization (n.)

3. **caus′tic** (kôs′tĭk), *adj.* [From Greek *kaustikos* capable of burning, corrosive.]

   Capable of burning, corroding, or destroying tissue by chemical action.

   The *caustic* cleaning fluid, which she had spilled, ate a hole in the carpet.

   Cutting or sarcastic in utterance.

   Caustic remarks by thoughtless Christians can give Christianity a bad name.

   Synonyms: corrosive, acidic, cankerous; sardonic, scathing, excoriating
   Antonyms: restorative, healing; kind, cordial, amiable, gracious
   Related forms: caustically (adv.), caustic (n.), causticity (n.)

4. **cri•te′ri•on** (krī•têr′ĭ•ĭn), *n.* [From Greek *kriterion* a means for judging, from *krites* judge.]

   A test, rule, or standard by which something is judged.

   The Bible is the *criterion* by which every action of a person's life should be measured.

   Synonyms: touchstone, yardstick, gauge, barometer, guideline, norm
   Related form: criteriology (n.)

5. **del′e•te′ri•ous** (dĕl′ĕ•têr′ĭ•us), *adj.* [From Greek *deleterios* harmful, from *deleter* destroyer, from *deleisthai* to hurt.]

   Physically or morally harmful.

   It has now been indisputably proved that tobacco smoking has a *deleterious* effect upon one's health.

   Synonyms: injurious, hurtful, ruinous, noxious, baneful, detrimental
   Antonyms: salutary, healthful, beneficial, salubrious, constructive
   Related forms: deleteriously (adv.), deleteriousness (n.)

Units
5

6. **dem′a•gogue** (dĕm′ə•gŏg), *n.* [From Greek *demagogos* popular leader: *demos* common people + *agogos* leading.]

    A leader who appeals to the emotions and prejudices of the populace in order to obtain power.

    One should beware of the sensational claims, the specious arguments, and the blarney of *demagogues:* after their election, they quickly set out to do as they please, rather than carry out their promises.

    Synonyms: agitator, haranguer, rabble-rouser
    Related forms: demagogic or demogogical (adj.), demagogism (n.), demagogy (n.)

7. **ep′i•thet** (ĕp′*i*•thĕt), *n.* [From Greek *epitheton* something added, from *epitithenai* to place upon: *epi-* upon + *tithenai* to place.]

    A name or title used to describe or characterize a person or thing.

    The *epithet* Honest Abe was used to characterize the integrity of our nation's sixteenth President.

    Synonyms: appellation, designation, label, nickname
    Related forms: epithetic or epithetical (adj.)

8. **id′i•o•syn′cra•sy** (ĭd′•ĭ•ō•sĭng′krə•əsĭ), *n.* [From Greek *idiosunkrasia* a peculiar temperament: *idios* one's own + *sun* with + *krasis* a blending.]

    A temperament peculiar to an individual; any personal peculiarity or mannerism.

    The putting of catsup on black-eyed peas seemed perfectly normal to him; to others it seemed a strange *idiosyncrasy.*

    Synonyms: eccentricity, peculiarity, singularity, oddity
    Antonyms: commonness, normality, ordinariness
    Related form: idiosyncratic (adj.)

9. **pan′a•ce′a** (păn′ə•sē′ə), *n.* [From Greek *panakeia: pan-* all + *akeisthai* to cure.]

    A supposed remedy for all diseases or ills.

    Before the sheriff ran him out of town, the mountebank had sold to some of the gullible townspeople several bottles of tonic, which he was vaunting as a wondrous *panacea.*

    Synonyms: cure-all, elixir, nostrum
    Related form: panacean (adj.)

10. **pleth′o•ra** (plĕth′ō•rə), *n.* [From Greek *plethora* fullness, from *plethein* to be full.]

    Excess; superabundance.

    The *plethora* of wealth accumulated during the Roaring Twenties vanished during the Depression.

    Synonyms: overfullness, superfluity, oversupply, profusion
    Antonyms: dearth, inadequacy, insufficiency, scantiness
    Related form: plethoric (adj.)

11. **pseu′do•nym** (sŭ′dȯ•nĭm), *n.* [From Greek *pseudonumon: pseudes* false + *onoma* name.]

    A fictitious name, as one assumed by an author.

    William Sydney Porter wrote his short stories under the *pseudonym* of O. Henry.

    Synonyms: pen name, nom de plume, cryptonym, alias
    Related forms: pseudonymity (n.), pseudonymous (adj.)

12. **spo•rad′ic** (spȯ•răd′ĭk), *adj.* [From *sporadikos,* from *sporas* scattered, from *sporos* sowing.]

    Occurring in occasional or isolated instances.

    Humanism and religion are thus, as historical facts, by no means parallel; humanism has been *sporadic,* but Christianity continuous. —*T. S. Eliot*

    Synonyms: occasional, infrequent, random, irregular, spotty
    Antonyms: regular, frequent, unremitting, unbroken
    Related form: sporadically (adv.)

EXERCISE A *From the list of vocabulary words in this unit, choose the one that best completes each of the following sentences. Write the word in the blank provided.*

1. Many drugs that seem so good in the first trials prove to have _____deleterious_____ aftereffects. —*Heiser*

2. A classic and infamous example of a(n) _____demagogue_____ is Adolf Hitler, who amazingly was able to hoodwink the German people.

3. Ask a(n)_____agnostic_____ if there is a God and he will say that we cannot know anything for certain.

4. There cannot be . . . an absolute _____panacea_____—a medicine that will cure every disease incident to the human body. —*Wesley*

5. At the first battle of Bull Run, the famous Confederate General Thomas J. Jackson received the _____epithet_____ Stonewall Jackson when he was observed "standing like a stone wall" against overwhelming odds.

6. Permanent tax reform will never be accomplished if there are only _____sporadic_____ outbursts of protest from the overburdened taxpayers.

7. Whereas in times past men read and mused over great and substantial works of literature, modern men, inundated with a(n) _____plethora_____ of amusements, are being robbed of the ability to think.

8. Although both the Jews and the Arabs are descendants of Abraham, the Jews remain a(n) _____anathema_____ to the Arabs.

9. Samuel Langhorne Clemens, better known by his _____pseudonym_____ , Mark Twain, is one of America's great authors.

10. Because the contestant failed to meet the primary _____criterion_____ set forth by the judges, he was disqualified from competition.

11. The immaculate housekeeper often surprised her guests with her pet _____idiosyncrasy_____: she would make them remove their shoes before they could enter.

12. A torrent of _____caustic_____ words can wound more deeply than a sword.

EXERCISE B *For each word in column **A**, select a word from column **B** that is most nearly a **synonym** of that word. Write its letter in the blank provided.*

	A		B
c	**1.** caustic	**a.**	yardstick
d	**2.** deleterious	**b.**	appellation
h	**3.** plethora	**c.**	corrosive
b	**4.** epithet	**d.**	noxious
l	**5.** panacea	**e.**	infidel
e	**6.** agnostic	**f.**	haranguer
k	**7.** pseudonym	**g.**	eccentricity
f	**8.** demagogue	**h.**	oversupply
a	**9.** criterion	**i.**	random
i	**10.** sporadic	**j.**	cordial
m	**11.** anathema	**k.**	nom de plume
g	**12.** idiosyncrasy	**l.**	elixir
		m.	abhorrence
		n.	believer

EXERCISE C *Word Analysis.*

1. *Learn the meanings of the following word parts.*

<table>
<tr><td>

Prefixes:

ana- (an-) up, back, again

ec- out, out of

epi- (ep-) upon, out-side, beyond

pan- all

</td><td>

Roots:

ANTHROP man, human being

CEDE, CEED, CESS to go, to yield

DEM(O) people

LEG, LECT, LIG to choose, to gather, to read

NOMEN, NOMIN, NOM name

PHIL to love

RUPT to break

SERV to serve, to protect, to save

</td><td>

Suffixes:

-acy -cy state, quality, act of

-ery, -ry state, quality, act of

-ice state, quality, act of

-otic pertaining to, having the quality of

</td></tr>
</table>

Units 5

2. *Using the Word Analyzer (inside the front and back covers), write down the literal meaning of the following words. First, write the meanings of the various parts; next, rearrange the wording of the parts to formulate a good definition.*

bibliophilistic	BIBLI(O)	ROOT	=	book
	PHIL	ROOT	=	to love
	-ist	SUFFIX	=	one who
	-ic	SUFFIX	=	like, pertaining to
		DEFINITION	=	pertaining to one who loves books
interruption	inter-	PREFIX	=	between, among
	RUPT	ROOT	=	to break
	-ion	SUFFIX	=	state, quality, act of, -ing
		DEFINITION	=	act of breaking between
innominable	in-²	PREFIX	=	not
	NOMIN	ROOT	=	name
	-able	SUFFIX	=	able to (be)
		DEFINITION	=	not able to be named

Everyday Expressions

Cynic

In the word "cynic" is embodied a true figure of speech, since it represents in its present use a radical departure from the original meaning of the word. "Cynic" is the English form of the Greek word that means "doglike." Nowadays a cynic is a person who disbelieves in human goodness or the possibility of a man or woman acting from other than selfish motives.

The Cynics of history were a set of Greek philosophers founded by Antisthenes, a disciple of Socrates, about 400 B.C. Their name is derived either from the place where they usually taught, the Cyno-sarges, or the Greek word "kunos," a dog, in derision of their morose, snarling principles, and intense scorn for all the conventions, and even humanity at large. For the early Cynics, virtue alone was the highest good, and therefore both learning and pleasure were things contemptible.

EXERCISE D *Verbal Analogies. In each of the following questions, a related pair of words or phrases is followed by five lettered pairs of words or phrases. Select the pair that best expresses a relationship similar to that expressed in the original pair. Circle the letter of your answer. [How to understand analogies is explained on pages 10–12.]*

1. SNOW : FLAKE ::

  (a) pie : pan
  (b) jelly : jar
  (c) hail : stones
  (d) ice : skate
  (e) coffee : urn

Snow falls in flakes; hail falls in stones.

2. ALUMNI : ALUMNAE ::

  (a) sisters : brothers
  (b) woman : man
  (c) crack : crevice
  (d) rams : ewes
  (e) restaurant : restaurants
       (see below)

3. EPITHET : APPELLATION ::

  (a) deleterious : injurious
  (b) plethora : inadequacy
  (c) idiosyncrasy : singularity
  (d) sporadic : infrequent
  (e) malediction : anathematize
       (see below)

> *Sarcasm is the language of the devil; for which reason I have long since as good as renounced it.*
> —Thomas Carlyle

EXERCISE E *Write an original sentence with each of the following words.* **Answers will vary.**

1. caustic _____

_____

_____

2. deleterious _____

_____

_____

3. demagogue _____

_____

_____

4. plethora _____

_____

_____

5. sporadic _____

_____

_____

2. *Alumni* is the plural for male graduates, and *alumnae* is the plural for female graduates. *Rams* is the plural for male sheep; *ewes* is the plural for female sheep.

3. *Epithet* and *appellation* are synonyms and nouns; *idiosyncrasy* and *singularity* are synonyms and nouns.

UNIT 6

Lethargy *(Word History)*

Greek mythology tells us of *Lethe,* a river in Hades, whose water when drunk caused forgetfulness of the past. John Milton in *Paradise Lost* called it "Lethe the river of oblivion." From *Lethe* "forgetfulness" and *argos* "idle, lazy" the Greeks formed the word *lethargos* "forgetful." The word passed through Latin as *lethargia* and French as *lethargie.* It came into English in the fourteenth century spelled variously as *literge, litarge, litargy,* and *lytargye.* During the sixteenth century it assumed its current spelling *lethargy.* Today anyone in a condition of *lethargy* acts as though he were sleepy. He is in a state of sluggishness, inertness, or apathy.

PRE-TEST *In each group below, circle the letter of the word that is nearest in meaning to the word at the left. Then check your answers to see how you rate.*

1. **discomfit**   (a) entreat   (b) surrender   (c) nullify   (d) overthrow

2. **replete**   (a) dormant   (b) drained   (c) well-filled   (d) couchant

3. **retribution**   (a) abnegation   (b) protestation   (c) condemnation   (d) forgiveness

4. **coerce**   (a) cajole   (b) compel   (c) conquer   (d) certify

5. **reprehensible**   (a) blameworthy   (b) laudatory   (c) blameless   (d) remonstratory

6. **reticence**   (a) assertion   (b) reserve   (c) openness   (d) agreement

7. **remonstrance**   (a) continuity   (b) agreement   (c) frankness   (d) objection

8. **respite**   (a) recess   (b) revenge   (c) activity   (d) taciturnity

9. **corroborate**   (a) persuade   (b) contradict   (c) substantiate   (d) submit

10. **reprisal**   (a) expostulation   (b) reconciliation   (c) execution   (d) retaliation

11. **renunciation**   (a) demand   (b) surrender   (c) consent   (d) vengeance

12. **recumbent**   (a) reclining   (b) plenary   (c) standing   (d) drained

NUMBER CORRECT ☐   **RATING** ☐ Extraordinary   ☐ Excellent   ☐ Good
                                         11–12 correct   9–10 correct   7–8 correct

1. coerce	4. recumbent	7. replete	10. respite
2. corroborate	5. remonstrance	8. reprehensible	11. reticence
3. discomfit	6. renunciation	9. reprisal	12. retribution

1. **co•erce′** (kō•ûrs′), *v.* [From Latin *coercere:* *co-* together + *arcere* to shut up, confine, restrain.]
   To force someone to comply or obey, as by pressure, threats, or intimidation; to effect by force.
   The Roman government tried to *coerce* the Christians to deny Christ and worship Caesar.

   Synonyms: compel, constrain, oblige, extort, bully, draft
   Antonyms: persuade, coax, entreat, inveigle, blandish, cajole
   Related forms: coercer (n.), coercible (adj.), coercion (n.), coercive (adj.)

2. **cor•rob′o•rate** (ko•rŏb′ŏ•rāt), *v.* [From Latin *corroboratus,* from *corroborare* to strengthen: *com-* *(cor-)* together + *roborare* to make strong.]
   To strengthen or confirm by agreeing statements or new evidence.
   He recollected Rip at once, and *corroborated* his story in the most satisfactory manner. —*Irving*

   Synonyms: substantiate, verify, authenticate, validate, certify, document
   Antonyms: contradict, invalidate, negate, nullify
   Related forms: corroborant (n.), corroboration (n.), corroborative (adj.), corroborator (n.), corroboratory (adj.)

3. **dis•com′fit** (dĭs•kŭm′fĭt), *v.* [From Latin *disconficere:* *dis-* reversal + *conficere* to prepare, accomplish: *com-* *(con-)* together + *facere* to make.]
   To defeat completely, overthrow, rout.
   The Lord *discomfited* them [the Amorites] before Israel, and slew them with a great slaughter at Gibeon. —*Josh. 10:10*

   To thwart the plans or purposes of; to throw into confusion.
   Odysseus *discomfited* the Sirens by stopping the ears of his men with wax and having himself tied to the mast of his ship so that the Sirens' sweet song would not lure them to destruction.

   Synonyms: vanquish, conquer, overcome, rout; frustrate, foil, hinder
   Antonyms: surrender, submit, succumb; fulfill, effect, accomplish
   Related forms: discomfiture (n.), discomfiter (n.)

4. **re•cum′bent** (rē•kŭm′bent), *adj.* [From Latin *recumbens,* from *recumbere* to lie down: *re-* back, again + *cumbere* to lie.]
   Reclining; lying down; resting.
   The ten Iroquois . . . glided like shadows into the midst of the camp, where, by the dull glow of the smoldering fires, they could distinguish the *recumbent* figures of their victims.
   —*Francis Parkman*

   Synonyms: prone, supine, prostrate, couchant, dormant
   Antonyms: upright, erect, standing
   Related forms: recumbently (adv.), recumbency (n.)

5. **re•mon′strance** (rē•mŏn′strans), *n.* [From Medieval Latin *remonstrare* to demonstrate: *re-* again + *monstrare* to show.]
   The act of objecting or protesting.
   The President yielded to the *remonstrance* of his foreign policy adviser and canceled his trip overseas.

   Synonyms: expostulation, objection, protestation
   Antonyms: acquiescence, consent, assent, agreement
   Related forms: remonstrate (v.), remonstrant (n.), remonstrantly (adv.), remonstration (n.), remonstrative (adj.), remonstrator (n.), remonstratory (adj.)

6. **re•nun′ci•a′tion** (rĕ•nŭn′sĭ•ā′shŭn), *n.* [From Latin *renuntiare* to protest against: *re-* back, against + *nuntiare* to report.]

 The act of formally or voluntarily giving up a claim or title.

   King Edward VIII's *renunciation* of the throne of England in order to marry the divorcee Wallis Simpson disgraced the rest of the royal family.

   Synonyms: abnegation, self-abnegation, self-denial, sacrifice, surrender
   Antonyms: assertion, claim, demand
   Related forms: renounce (v.), renunciative (adj.), renunciatory (adj.)

7. **re•plete′** (rĕ•plēt′), *adj.* [From Latin *replere* to refill: *re-* again + *plere* to fill.]

 Abundantly supplied; well-filled.

   Michelangelo—Italian painter, sculptor, poet, and architect—was *replete* with talent: he is known as one of the greatest artists of the Renaissance.

   Synonyms: full, complete, plenary, bountiful
   Antonyms: empty, drained, insufficient
   Related forms: repleteness (n.), repletion (n.)

8. **rep′re•hen′si•ble** (rĕp′rĕ•hĕn′si•b'l), *adj.* [From Latin *reprehendere* rebuke, hold back: *re-* back + *prehendere* to seize.]

 Deserving of blame, rebuke, or censure.

   Paul thought Mark's desertion at Pamphylia *reprehensible* and refused to take him on another missionary journey.

   Synonyms: blameworthy, reprovable, condemnable
   Antonyms: commendable, laudatory, blameless
   Related forms: reprehensibly (adv.), reprehension (n.), reprehensibleness (n.)

9. **re•pris′al** (rĕ•prīz′al; ′l), *n.* [From Latin *reprehendere* rebuke, hold back: *re-* back + *prehendere* to seize.]

 Forcible seizure in retaliation for injuries received; injury done in return for injury received.

   Israeli jets bombed Lebanon in *reprisal* for repeated attacks upon Israel.

   Synonyms: retaliation, revenge, counterattack
   Antonyms: reconciliation, compromise, submission
   Related form: reprise (n.)

10. **res′pite** (rĕs′pĭt), *n.* [From Latin *respectus* a looking back, from *respicere*: *re-* back + *specere* to look.]

 An interval of relief or rest; a delay of punishment.

   He went to his creditor and said, "I am sorry that I cannot pay you right now; but if you will give me a month's *respite,* I will discharge my debt in full."

   Synonyms: pause, recess, lull, intermission, postponement, suspension
   Antonyms: continuity, activity, movement; action, execution
   Related form: respiteless (n.)

11. **ret′i•cence** (rĕt′i•sens; -s'ns), *n.* [From Latin *reticere* to keep silent: *re-* again + *tacere* to be silent.]

 Inclination to be silent.

   Divine wisdom betrays itself by *reticence* about the unseen world. —*J. Tait*

   Synonyms: silence, reserve, taciturnity, uncommunicativeness
   Antonyms: frankness, openness, ingenuousness, talkativeness
   Related form: reticent (adj.)

12. **ret′ri•bu′tion** (rĕt′ri•bū′shŭn), *n.* [From Latin *retribuere* to pay back: *re-* back + *tribuere* to grant, pay.]

 Punishment for offenses; compensation.

   The Bible warns of eternal *retribution* for those who reject Christ as savior: they "shall be punished with everlasting destruction from the presence of the Lord, and from the glory of his power." —*2 Thess. 1:9*

   Synonyms: condemnation, chastisement, discipline
   Antonyms: forgiveness, pardoning, acquittal, overlooking
   Related forms: retributive (adj.), retributor (n.), retributory (adj.)

EXERCISE A   *From the list of vocabulary words in this unit, choose the one that best completes each of the following sentences. Write the word in the blank provided.*

1. "And the Lord ____discomfited____ Sisera, and all his chariots, and all his host, with the edge of the sword before Barak; so that Sisera lighted down off his chariot, and fled away on his feet." —*Judges 4:15*

2. Rather than discussing your financial affairs with others, it is usually best to maintain your ____reticence____ concerning such personal matters.

3. For severe hemorrhaging, put the patient in a ____recumbent____ position, raise the wounded part of the body, place a sterile cloth on the wound, and press the wound firmly with your hand.

4. Over the ____remonstrances____ of her family and friends, she had married an unsaved boy, and now she was reaping the bitter consequences.

5. Sometimes World War I and World War II are thought of as one long war with a ____respite____ of less than twenty years between.

6. The speculations of evolutionists concerning the origin of the world have not been and never will be ____corroborated____ .

7. On July 28, 1914, Austria-Hungary declared war on Serbia in ____reprisal____ for the shooting of Archduke Francis Ferdinand, heir to the throne of Austria-Hungary.

8. At the beginning of World War II, the Axis Powers were ____replete____ with armed forces and factories with which to build war materials.

9. Because it is taught in the Bible, Christians believe that the death penalty is just____retribution____ for a murderer.

10. In 1215, a group of barons ____coerced____ King John of England to sign the Magna Charta, a great document, in which is rooted the concept of individual liberties.

11. Moses' ____renunciation____ of Egyptian power and wealth was evidence of his eternal, rather than temporal, values.

12. The ____reprehensible____ actions of criminals should not be condoned under the pretext of temporary insanity.

> *He that doeth wrong shall receive for the wrong which he hath done: and there is no respect of persons.*
> —*Col. 3:25*

EXERCISE B *For each word in column* **A,** *select a word from column* **B** *that is most nearly an* **antonym** *of that word. Write its letter in the blank provided.*

	A		B
l	**1.** replete	**a.**	succumb
h	**2.** reticence	**b.**	reconciliation
j	**3.** respite	**c.**	entreat
b	**4.** reprisal	**d.**	acquittal
a	**5.** discomfit	**e.**	silence
n	**6.** renunciation	**f.**	commendable
f	**7.** reprehensible	**g.**	erect
g	**8.** recumbent	**h.**	talkativeness
k	**9.** remonstrance	**i.**	contradict
d	**10.** retribution	**j.**	action
i	**11.** corroborate	**k.**	acquiescence
c	**12.** coerce	**l.**	empty
		m.	objection
		n.	claim

EXERCISE C *Word Analysis.*

1. *Learn the meanings of the following word parts.*

Prefixes:

com- (co-, col-, con-, cor-) with, together

dis- (di-, dif-) apart, away, not

hyper- over, above, beyond

re- back, again

Roots:

ARCH chief, first, to rule

CUMB, CUB to lie (down)

FAC, FACT, FECT, FIC to do, to make

GER, GEST to bear, to carry, to produce

HYDR water

PHOB to fear

SCRIB, SCRIPT to write

THE, THEO god

Suffixes:

-age state, quality, act of

-ence, -ance, -ency, -ancy state, quality, act of

-ible able to (be)

-tion, ion state, quality, act of, -ing

2. *Using the Word Analyzer, write down the literal meaning of the following words. First, write the meanings of the various parts; next, rearrange the wording of the parts to formulate a good definition.*

hydrophobic	HYDR(O)	ROOT	=	water
	PHOB	ROOT	=	to fear
	-ic	SUFFIX	=	like, pertaining to
		DEFINITION	=	pertaining to the fear of water
convention	com- (con-)	PREFIX	=	with, together
	VEN	ROOT	=	to come
	-tion	SUFFIX	=	state, quality, act of, -ing
		DEFINTION	=	act of coming together
gestation	GEST(A)	ROOT	=	to bear, to carry, to produce
	-tion	SUFFIX	=	state, quality, act of, -ing
		DEFINITION	=	act of carrying

Units 6

41

EXERCISE D *Look up the word* confirm *in Webster's New Dictionary of Synonyms. Under that word, you will find discriminating explanations for the following words:* confirm, corroborate, *and* substantiate. *After studying these words, decide which of these three words best completes each of the following sentences.*

1. Ivan Pavlov, a Russian physiologist, conducted many experiments to ____substantiate____ his theory of conditional reflex.

2. His failure to complete the work on time ____confirmed____ our suspicion that he was not very reliable.

3. The student's story ____corroborated____ what we had already heard from several others.

EXERCISE E *Write an original sentence with each of the following words.* **Answers will vary.**

1. coerce _____

_____

_____

2. discomfit _____

_____

_____

3. remonstrance _____

_____

_____

4. respite _____

_____

_____

5. retribution _____

_____

_____

> *When Pharaoh saw that there was respite, he hardened his heart, and hearkened not unto them; as the Lord had said.* —Exo. 8:15

VOCABULARY REVIEW 2
(Units 1–6)

EXERCISE A *In each group below, circle the letter of the word that is most nearly a **synonym** of the word at the left.*

1. **emanate**   (a) permit   (b) derive   (c) hasten   (d) decrease
2. **clemency**   (a) relief   (b) frankness   (c) silence   (d) vengeance
3. **hiatus**   (a) uninterruption (b) respite   (c) objection   (d) appropriation
4. **agnostic**   (a) theist   (b) beggar   (c) unbeliever   (d) harbinger
5. **psuedonym**   (a) sacrifice   (b) touchstone   (c) elixir   (d) alias
6. **banal**   (a) loud   (b) destructive (c) pedestrian   (d) stimulating
7. **discomfit**   (a) surrender   (b) contradict   (c) rout   (d) coax
8. **impeccable**   (a) imperfect   (b) flawless   (c) harmless   (d) exposed
9. **lapidary**   (a) almsman   (b) gem engraver (c) herald   (d) threnody
10. **replete**   (a) clement   (b) penurious   (c) reprovable   (d) full
11. **plagiarism**   (a) appropriation (b) opulence   (c) privation   (d) damnation
12. **reticence**   (a) lacuna   (b) protection   (c) silence   (d) peculiarity
13. **chicanery**   (a) railing   (b) forthrightness (c) commendation (d) beguilement
14. **contumely**   (a) singularity (b) honor   (c) scorn   (d) cure-all
15. **demagogue**   (a) sanctioner   (b) atheist   (c) believer   (d) rabble-rouser
16. **sanction**   (a) condemnation (b) endorsement (c) guideline   (d) nickname
17. **expedient**   (a) essential   (b) cowardly   (c) chronic   (d) detrimental
18. **remonstrance** (a) consent   (b) obloquy   (c) eccentricity (d) protestation
19. **reprisal**   (a) compromise   (b) peculiarity (c) counterattack (d) superfluity
20. **epithet**   (a) protection   (b) designation (c) banishment   (d) norm

EXERCISE B *In each group below, circle the letter of the word that is most nearly an **antonym** of the word at the left.*

1. **obviate**   (a) terminate   (b) delay   (c) improve   (d) facilitate
2. **contumely**   (a) candor   (b) self-denial (c) easement   (d) adulation
3. **anathema**   (a) compensation (b) relief   (c) elegy   (d) benediction
4. **sporadic**   (a) infrequent   (b) corrosive   (c) regular   (d) cordial
5. **recumbent**   (a) dormant   (b) upright   (c) bountiful   (d) commendable
6. **heinous**   (a) appropriate (b) flippant   (c) virtuous   (d) captivating
7. **penury**   (a) mitigation   (b) luxury   (c) appropriation (d) retaliation
8. **reprehensible** (a) condemnable (b) empty   (c) corrosive   (d) blameless
9. **pestilent**   (a) harmless   (b) defenseless (c) humane   (d) destructive
10. **retribution**   (a) pardoning   (b) chastisement (c) recess   (d) action
11. **sanction**   (a) ratification (b) disapproval (c) arrogation   (d) interval
12. **idiosyncrasy** (a) self-denial (b) abhorrence   (c) normality   (d) joy
13. **frugality**   (a) wastefulness (b) theft   (c) mitigation   (d) severity
14. **incarcerate**   (a) teach   (b) confine   (c) release   (d) assimilate
15. **deleterious**   (a) hurtful   (b) healthful   (c) unbroken   (d) unremitting

EXERCISE C *In each group below, circle the letter of the word that is nearest in meaning to the expression in* **boldface type.**

1. waves . . . renewed their **funeral song** with every human life they swept away. —*Martineau*
   (a) fetish   (b) dirge   (c) epithet   (d) plethora

2. John the Baptist, the **one who heralded the coming** of Christ
   (a) entrepreneur   (b) precursor   (c) lapidary   (d) mendicant

3. wanting to reflect a **thoughtful and serious** mood in his music
   (a) plaintive   (b) pensive   (c) strident   (d) piquant

4. in countries where people are always **forced to comply or obey**
   (a) coerced   (b) incarcerated   (c) discomfited   (d) extirpated

5. a poor habit of making **cutting or sarcastic** remarks
   (a) piquant   (b) trenchant   (c) caustic   (d) virulent

6. foolishly disregarded the **objections or protests** of his parents
   (a) invectives   (b) anathemas   (c) remonstrances   (d) sanctions

7. had a tendency to talk in **loud, harsh, grating** tones
   (a) plaintive   (b) egregious   (c) caustic   (d) strident

8. driven to make **forcible seizures in retaliation** for the piracy on the high seas
   (a) sanctions   (b) remonstrances   (c) reprisals   (d) renunciations

9. a mode of trial established as a **test, rule, or standard** of truth and falsehood
   (a) precursor   (b) corroboration   (c) coercer   (d) criterion

10. the **mournful** meowing of a kitten
    (a) penitent   (b) pensive   (c) strident   (d) plaintive

11. the **superabundance** of knowledge contained in a large library
    (a) frugality   (b) plethora   (c) emanation   (d) exigency

12. Elisha, miraculously fed by a woman living in **extreme poverty**
    (a) penury   (b) sinecure   (c) reticence   (d) chicanery

13. **occasional or isolated** sniper fire from across the river
    (a) insurgent   (b) sporadic   (c) pestilent   (d) expedient

14. when the fields are **covered with water** by the Nile
    (a) emanated   (b) extirpated   (c) inundated   (d) imbibed

15. **strengthened or confirmed** the earlier testimony of the defendant
    (a) obviated   (b) vitiated   (c) remonstrated   (d) corroborated

16. often ate in a **lying down** position
    (a) vulnerable   (b) verdant   (c) recumbent   (d) replete

17. hotly pursued them and **defeated completely** their already weakened forces
    (a) lapidated   (b) obviated   (c) inundated   (d) discomfited

18. the queen's **formal giving up** of her right of succession
    (a) renunciation   (b) reprehension   (c) obviation   (d) vitiation

19. shabby pamphlets filled with angry **abusive terms**
    (a) pseudonyms   (b) emoluments   (c) invectives   (d) epithets

20. the **deserving of blame** negligence in punishing criminals
    (a) deleterious   (b) inveterate   (c) indomitable   (d) reprehensible

44

EXERCISE D   *From the following list of vocabulary words, choose the one that best completes each of the following sentences. Write the word in the blank provided.*

caustic	deleterious	inveterate	penury	renunciation
coerce	frugality	mendicant	plethora	respite
corroborate	heinous	panacea	precursor	virulent

1. Because of the _____plethora_____ of salt and other minerals in the Dead Sea, no fish can survive in its waters.

2. My narrative has no other tendency than to illustrate and _____corroborate_____ your own observations.
    —*Samuel Johnson*

3. The analgesic gave the cancer patient only a brief _____respite_____ before his pain bacame unbearable again.

4. That the family lived in abject _____penury_____ was readily inferred from their tattered clothing and evident malnutrition.

5. The whole country around Detroit was covered by a sea of fog, the _____precursor_____ of a hot and sultry day. —*Francis Parkman*

6. Juvenalian satire is a(n) _____caustic_____ type of satire, known for the biting, angry manner in which it points out the corruption and evil of men and institutions.

7. Cirrhosis, a disease of the liver, is just one of the _____deleterious_____ effects of drinking alcohol.

8. By _____inveterate_____ practice among most of the commercial nations of Europe, bills of lading have long been drawn . . . in sets of three or more. —*Bowen*

9. After Judas's _____heinous_____ betrayal of Christ for the price of a slave, he returned the money and hanged himself.

10. During the Korean War, the North Koreans and the Chinese used brainwashing to _____coerce_____ prisoners of war to defend Communist philosophy.

11. Failing to exercise _____frugality_____ led the prodigal son to the pigpen.

12. Because of his _____virulent_____ hatred of Alexander Hamilton, Aaron Burr challenged him to a duel; Hamilton was killed, and Burr, indicted for murder.

13. Tapping his cane on the pavement, a blind _____mendicant_____ tried to attract the sympathy of those who passed by.

14. Tom Sawyer's Aunt Polly believed that castor oil was a perfect _____panacea_____ for whatever ailed Tom.

15. The modernization of the Japanese government resulted from Emperor Hirohito's _____renunciation_____ of the divine right of emperors.

EXERCISE E *In each of the following analogies, a related pair of words or phrases is followed by five lettered pairs of words or phrases. Select the pair that best expresses a relationship similar to that expressed in the original pair. Circle the letter of your answer.*

1. INCARCERATE : LIBERATE ::
   (a) vapid : piquing
   (b) virulent : toxic
   (c) exigency : strait
   (d) vitiate : debase
   (e) obviate : permit
   (v : v; ant.)

2. HIATUS : CONTINUITY::1
   (a) plagiarism : theft
   (b) sanction : disapproval
   (c) relief : mitigation
   (d) frugality : thrift
   (e) banal : pedestrian
   (n : n; ant.)

3. CAUSTIC : CORDIAL ::
   (a) anathema : delight
   (b) criterion : gauge
   (c) theist : infidel
   (d) impeccable : fallible
   (e) demagogue : agitator
   (adj : adj; ant.)

4. AGNOSTICALLY : DEIST ::
   (a) anathematize : nuisance
   (b) idiosyncratic : oddity
   (c) haranguer : demagogy
   (d) infrequent : regular
   (e) caustically : causticity
   (adv : n; rel.)

5. DIRGE : ELEGY ::
   (a) strident : raucous
   (b) contempt : honor
   (c) clemently : relief
   (d) penury : luxury
   (e) avert : permit
   (Question pair same part of speech; answer pair same part of speech—though not the same part of speech as the question pair. syn.)

6. RETRIBUTORY : RETRIBUTION::
   (a) respite : activity
   (b) reticent : taciturnity
   (c) reprehensibly : reprovable
   (d) repletion : complete
   (e) remonstrate : consent
   (adj : n; rel.)

EXERCISE F *Match each prefix, root, or suffix in column **A** with its definition in column **B**. Some definitions may be used more than once.*

	A		B
q	1. hyper-	a.	first, original, primitive
z	2. PHIL	b.	apart, aside
h	3. PET, PETIT	c.	water
p	4. un-	d.	up, back, again
k	5. LEG, LECT, LIG	e.	result of
y	6. CUMB, CUB	f.	with, together
w	7. pan-	g.	feeling, suffering, disease
n	8. BIO	h.	to seek, to assail
c	9. HYDR	i.	two
d	10. ana-	j.	to break
t	11. -ible	k.	to choose, to gather, to read
b	12. se-	l.	state, quality, act of
g	13. PATH	m.	name
x	14. TOM	n.	life
s	15. pre-	o.	birth, race, kind, cause
u	16. -otic	p.	not
j	17. RUPT	q.	over, above, beyond
l	18. -ice	r.	god
a	19. PROTO	s.	before
f	20. com-	t.	able to (be)
m	21. NOMEN, NOMIN, NOM	u.	pertaining to, having the quality of
o	22. GEN, GENIT	v.	true
l	23. -ism	w.	all
r	24. THE, THEO	x.	to cut, a section
i	25. di-	y.	to lie (down)
		z.	to love

EXERCISE G *Word Analysis. The following words contain prefixes, roots, and suffixes that you have memorized. Write down from memory the literal meanings of these words. First, write the meanings of the various parts; next, rearrange the wording of the parts to formulate a good definition.*

compensation

com-	PREFIX	=	with, together
PENS	ROOT	=	to hang, to weigh, to pay
-(a)tion	SUFFIX	=	state, quality, act of, -ing
	DEFINITION	=	a weighing together [a balancing]

seceder

se-	PREFIX	=	apart, aside
CED(E)	ROOT	=	to go, to yield
-er	SUFFIX	=	one who, that which
	DEFINITION	=	one who goes aside (or apart)

recurrence

re-	PREFIX	=	back, again
CUR(R)	ROOT	=	to run, to go
-ence	SUFFIX	=	state, quality, act of
	DEFINITION	=	act of running back (again)

philanthropism

PHIL	ROOT	=	to love
ANTHROP	ROOT	=	man, human being
-ism	SUFFIX	=	state, quality, act of
	DEFINITION	=	state of loving human beings

anatomy

ana-	PREFIX	=	up, back, again
TOM	ROOT	=	to cut, a section
-y	SUFFIX	=	state, quality, act, result of
	DEFINITION	=	act of cutting up

Units 1–6

Everyday Expressions

Mills of God

The idea contained in the figure of speech which represents the ruling power of the universe as presiding over a great mill, in which the destinies of mankind are ground, is very ancient, and is found in many ages and in many literatures. It seems to have seized on the minds of man everywhere and at all times as possessing a singular power and appositeness.

Probably the most familiar expression of the thought is found in the lines which Longfellow translated from Friedrich von Logau, a German poet of the seventeenth century, as follows:

"The mills of God grind slowly,
   yet they grind exceeding small;
Though with patience He stands waiting,
With exactness He grinds all."

One authority on words and phrases defines the expression, "The mills of God grind slowly," as follows: "Vengeance may be delayed, but it will come when least expected."

UNIT 7

Quixotic (Word History)

When fantastic tales of chivalry persisted in the Spanish literature of the late sixteenth and early seventeenth centuries, Miguel de Cervantes determined to write a satire ridiculing those fanciful tales. The hero of Cervantes's story was named Don Quixote. In the story, Quixote became so captivated by the romantic tales of chivalry that he decided to become a knight-errant and perform gallant deeds himself. He sallied forth on his scrawny horse Rosinante looking for high adventure. He determined to right wrongs and rescue those in distress. When adventures were not forthcoming, Quixote made his own. For example, his first adventure was a battle with a windmill, the sails of which he imagined to be the arms of a giant. After many such ludicrous adventures, Quixote returned home, feeble and broken, admitting that knight-errantry was impractical nonsense. From him we have gained the colorful word *quixotic,* which describes a person whose visionary ideas are absurdly impractical.

Unit
7

PRE-TEST *In each group below, circle the letter of the word that is nearest in meaning to the word at the left. Then check your answers to see how you rate.*

1. **parsimonious** (a) prodigal   (b) sarcastic   (c) stingy   (d) gentle
2. **propitious** (a) agreeable   (b) contrary   (c) surly   (d) dishonest
3. **querulous** (a) patient   (b) untruthful   (c) complaining   (d) miserly
4. **sedulous** (a) idle   (b) lavish   (c) agreeable   (d) diligent
5. **acrimonious** (a) bland   (b) bitter   (c) scrupulous   (d) peevish
6. **posthumous** (a) industrious   (b) inauspicious   (c) after-death   (d) brusque
7. **salubrious** (a) healthful   (b) deleterious   (c) secret   (d) open
8. **mendacious** (a) honest   (b) abrasive   (c) flattering   (d) lying
9. **pusillanimous** (a) stouthearted   (b) fainthearted   (c) irascible   (d) veracious
10. **surreptitious** (a) underhanded   (b) overt   (c) daring   (d) unfavorable
11. **noxious** (a) corrupting   (b) wholesome   (c) choleric   (d) trustworthy
12. **unctuous** (a) rough   (b) oily   (c) healthful   (d) unconcealed

NUMBER CORRECT ☐   **RATING** ☐ Extraordinary   ☐ Excellent   ☐ Good
                                                 11–12 correct   9–10 correct   7–8 correct

49

1. acrimonious	4. parsimonious	7. pusillanimous	10. sedulous
2. mendacious	5. posthumous	8. querulous	11. surreptitious
3. noxious	6. propitious	9. salubrious	12. unctuous

1. **ac′ri•mo′ni•ous** (ăk′ri•mō′nĭ•us), *adj.* [From Latin *acrimonia* pungency, from *acris* sharp, pungent + *-ous* having the quality of.]
   Harsh or bitter in disposition, speech, or manner.
   > Christian principles defended in an *acrimonious* manner can cause the truth to become odious to those who need it most.

   Synonyms: caustic, sarcastic, surly, irascible, choleric
   Antonyms: bland, gentle, mild, genial, gracious
   Related forms: acrimoniously (adv.), acrimoniousness (n.), acrimony (n.)

2. **men•da′cious** (mĕn•dā′shus), *adj.* [From Latin *mendax, mendacis* lying, false.]
   Lying; false.
   > While the communication was deceptive and so intended, it was not technically *mendacious.* —*S. H. Adams*

   Synonyms: dishonest, untruthful, deceitful, prevaricating
   Antonyms: veracious, honest, scrupulous, trustworthy
   Related forms: mendaciously (adv.), mendaciousness (n.), mendacity (n.)

3. **nox′ious** (nŏk′shus) *adj.* [From Latin *noxious,* from *noxa* harm, injury.]
   Physically or morally harmful.
   > Because the derailed train included several tank cars filled with *noxious* chemicals, over half of the nearby town had to be evacuated.

   Synonyms: baneful, pernicious, deleterious, corrupting, injurious
   Antonyms: wholesome, sanitary, salubrious, healthful, beneficial
   Related forms: noxiously (adv.), noxiousness (n.)

4. **par′si•mo′ni•ous** (pär′si•mō′nĭ•us), *adj.* [From Latin *parcimonia,* from *parcere* to spare.]
   Overcareful in spending; stingy.
   > Ebenezer Scrooge of Dickens's *Christmas Carol* was so *parsimonious* that he loathed to let his employees off even for Christmas Day.

   Synonyms: penurious, tightfisted, miserly
   Antonyms: prodigal, profuse, lavish, openhanded, generous
   Related forms: parsimoniously (adv.), parsimoniousness (n.), parsimony (n.)

5. **post′hu•mous** (pŏs′tŭ•mus), *adj.* [From Latin *postumus* last, late-born (superlative of *post* after): erroneously altered in Late Latin to *posthumus* after *humus* ground or *humare* to bury, as if meaning "born after the father is buried."]
   Occurring or appearing after one's death (as a child born after the death of its father, or a writing published after the death of the author).
   > The book was a *posthumous* work which could well have used the judicious author's hand in its final draft.

   Synonyms: after-death, post-mortem, post-obit
   Related forms: posthumously (adv.)

6. **pro•pi′tious** (prŏ•pĭsh′us), *adj.* [From Latin *propitius* favorable: *pro-* before + *petere* to rush forward.]
   Favorably inclined; gracious.
   > Jacob attempted to render his brother Esau *propitious* by sending him presents.

   Synonyms: agreeable, well-disposed, auspicious, beneficent
   Antonyms: contrary, averse, opposed, unfavorable, inauspicious
   Related forms: propitiously (adv.), propitiousness (n.)

7. **pu′sil•lan′i•mous** (pū′si•lăn′i•mus), adj. [From Latin *pusillanimis,* from *pusillus* weak + *animus* spirit.]

> ***Lacking in courage; characterized by weakness of spirit.***
>
> One of the men said to the other, "Don't be so *pusillanimous;* if you were supposed to receive a pocket calculator when you opened your account, go ask the teller for it."
>
> *Synonyms:* fainthearted, cowardly, mean-spirited, craven
> *Antonyms:* stouthearted, daring, courageous, brave
> *Related forms:* pusillanimously (adv.), pusillanimity (n.)

8. **quer′u•lous** (kwĕr′ŭ•lus), adj. [From Latin *querulus* complaining, from *queri* to complain.]
> ***Given to complaining; full of complaints.***
>
> It is not good for Christians to be *querulous,* when God has done so much for us.
>
> *Synonyms:* fretful, whining, peevish, petulant, waspish, irritable
> *Antonyms:* patient, forbearing, content, easygoing, good-natured, satisfied
> *Related forms:* querulously (adv.), querulousness (n.)

> *Who art thou that repliest against God? Shall the thing formed say to him that formed it, Why hast thou made me thus?* —Rom. 9:20

9. **sa•lu′bri•ous** (sə•lū′brĭ•us), adj. [From Latin *salubris* promoting health, from *salus* welfare, health.]
> ***Promoting health or well-being.***
>
> Many people suffering from gout attested to the *salubrious* effect of the mineral waters at Bath.
>
> *Synonyms:* healthful, wholesome, salutary, beneficial
> *Antonyms:* deleterious, detrimental, noxious, harmful
> *Related forms:* salubriousness (n.), salubrity (n.), salubriously (adv.)

10. **sed′u•lous** (sĕd′ŭ•lus), adj. [From Latin *sedulus* busy, from *sedulo: se-* apart from + *dolus* guile.]
> ***Diligent, hard-working, persistent.***
>
> *Sedulous* attention and painstaking industry always mark the true worker. —*Smiles*
>
> *Synonyms:* industrious, busy, assiduous, studious
> *Antonyms:* idle, unoccupied, lazy, slothful
> *Related forms:* sedulously (adv.), sedulousness (n.), sedulity (n.)

11. **sur′rep•ti′tious** (sûr′ĕp•tĭsh′us), adj. [From Latin *surrepticius,* from *surripere* to take away secretly: *sub- (sur-)* secretly + *rapere* to seize.]
> ***Taken or done stealthily or secretly; unauthorized.***
>
> The *surreptitious* removal of Mary Stuart from Scotland was frowned upon by Elizabeth of England.
>
> *Synonyms:* underhanded, secret, covert, furtive, clandestine
> *Antonyms:* overt, open, unconcealed, aboveboard
> *Related forms:* surreptitiously (adv.), surreptitiousness (n.)

12. **unc′tu•ous** (ŭngk′tŭ•us), adj. [From Latin *unctum* ointment, from *unguere* to annoint.]
> ***Oily or greasy.***
>
> This fish takes the name of sea snail from the soft and *unctuous* texture of its body, resembling that of the land snail. —*Pennant*
>
> ***Insincerely suave or oily in speech or manner.***
>
> The Pardoner of the *Canterbury Tales* fooled many people with his *unctuous* manner and counterfeit sacraments.
>
> *Synonyms:* oily, greasy, slippery, soapy; smooth, fulsome, flattering
> *Antonyms:* nongreasy, rough, abrasive; gruff, harsh, brusque
> *Related forms:* unctuously (adv.), unctuousness (n.), unctuosity (n.)

EXERCISE A *From the list of vocabulary words in this unit, choose the one that best completes each of the following sentences. Write the word in the blank provided.*

1. Through _____ sedulous _____ practice, a student can learn to speak a foreign language fluently.

2. The _____ unctuous _____ manner of the politician disgusted us.

3. In India, some people still attempt to render their gods _____ propitious _____ by casting their babies into the Ganges River.

4. Ananias and Sapphira, for their _____ mendacious _____ claim that they had given the full price of the land to God, were both struck dead within three hours.

5. When angry, one must be careful to guard his tongue: the continuing ill effects of _____ acrimonious _____ words can seldom if ever be totally erased.

6. The faulty exhaust system of the old car allowed the _____ noxious _____ carbon monoxide fumes to overcome the unwary driver.

7. The _____ posthumous _____ publication of Emily Dickinson's poetry was a decision made by Emily's sister, Lavinia.

8. _____ Salubrious _____ mountain air was what the doctor recommended for his asthmatic patient.

9. Because of the Lord's innumerable blessings to us, we should not be _____ parsimonious _____ in our giving to Him.

10. Because of his fear of the Pharisees, Nicodemus made a(n) _____ surreptitious _____ visit to Christ by night.

11. Whenever the schoolteacher called a home to enlist the aid of the parents in correcting their recalcitrant child, she often received a(n) _____ pusillanimous _____ reply such as this from the father: "You'll have to talk to my wife about that; she handles all those matters."

12. Because she could not satisfy the _____ querulous _____ patient, the nurse avoided walking past his room.

EXERCISE B *In each group below, circle the letter of the word that is either a **synonym** or an **antonym** of the word at the left.*

1. **noxious**   (a) bland   (b) dishonest   (c) trustworthy   (d) beneficial

2. **querulous**   (a) assiduous   (b) forbearing   (c) tightfisted   (d) caustic

3. **posthumous**   (a) post-obit   (b) wholesome   (c) injurious   (d) miserly

4. **surreptitious**   (a) waspish   (b) unconcealed   (c) inauspicious   (d) brave

5. **mendacious**   (a) contrary   (b) stouthearted   (c) deceitful   (d) fretful

6. **unctuous**   (a) gruff   (b) patient   (c) whining   (d) wholesome

7. **salubrious**   (a) irritable   (b) easygoing   (c) industrious   (d) harmful

8. **propitious**   (a) slothful   (b) well-disposed   (c) aboveboard   (d) smooth

9. **sedulous**   (a) industrious   (b) surly   (c) mild   (d) corrupting

10. **acrimonious**   (a) non-greasy   (b) gentle   (c) open   (d) secret

11. **pusillanimous**   (a) studious   (b) courageous   (c) idle   (d) untruthful

12. **parsimonious**   (a) busy   (b) lazy   (c) veracious   (d) profuse

EXERCISE C *Word Analysis.*

1. *Learn the meanings of the following word parts.*

Prefixes:

a- (an-) not, without

en- (em-) in, into, causative

post- after

sub- under

Roots:

ART art, skill, craft

CERN, CRET to separate, to distinguish

CORD heart

FORT strong

MIT(T), MIS(S) to send, to let go

PHON sound, voice

RAP, RAPT to snatch, to seize

SEQU, SECUT to follow

Suffixes:

-ant one who, that which, -ing

-ory[1] like, pertaining to

-ory,[2] *orium* place where, thing which

-ous, -ose having the quality of

2. *Using the Word Analyzer, write down the literal meaning of the following words. First, write the meanings of the various parts; next, rearrange the wording of the parts to formulate a good definition.*

raptorial	RAPT	ROOT	=	to snatch, to seize
	-or	SUFFIX	=	one who, that which
	-(i)al	SUFFIX	=	like, pertaining to
		DEFINITION	=	pertaining to one who (that which) seizes
excretory	ex-	PREFIX	=	out (of), away from, without, intensive
	CRET	ROOT	=	to separate, to distinguish
	-ory[1]	SUFFIX	=	like, pertaining to
		DEFINITION	=	pertaining to separating out of
atheistic	a-	PREFIX	=	not, without
	THE	ROOT	=	god
	-ist	SUFFIX	=	one who
	-ic	SUFFIX	=	like, pertaining to
		DEFINITION	=	pertaining to one who is without God

EXERCISE D *For each of the following words, list the antonyms given in this lesson.*

1. acrimonious bland, gentle, mild, genial, gracious

2. noxious wholesome, sanitary, salubrious, healthful, beneficial

3. parsimonious prodigal, profuse, lavish, openhanded, generous

4. pusillanimous stouthearted, daring, courageous, brave

5. querulous patient, forbearing, content, easygoing, good-natured, satisfied

Unit 7

53

EXERCISE E *Write an original sentence with each of the following words.* **Answers will vary.**

1. mendacious _____

_____

_____

2. posthumous _____

_____

_____

3. propitious _____

_____

_____

4. surreptitious _____

_____

_____

5. unctuous _____

_____

_____

Everyday Expressions

Sour Grapes

The use of the expression, "sour grapes," is very common—it is, indeed, one of our most familiar, everyday figures of speech, being used by young and old alike. It is known not only in the English language, but in others.

Its origin is the story told in Aesop's "Fables" of the fox who tried in vain to reach some grapes growing on a wall, and finally gave up in disgust, saying, "Oh, well, those grapes are sour, anyway!" In that way "sour grapes" acquired its definition as "something which is beyond our reach, and which we therefore belittle and declare to be of no value." One authority declares "sour grapes" to be "things despised because they are beyond our reach; many men of low degree call titles and dignities 'sour grapes,' and men of no parts turn up their noses at literary honors."

Mrs. Gaskell, in the novel *Cranford*, speaks of "a sort of sour grapeism, which made us very peaceful and satisfied."

UNIT 8

Melancholy (Word History)

According to the ancient humoral theory, a person's body contained four humors, or body fluids: blood, phlegm, yellow bile, and black bile. An excess of any one of the humors was believed to account for the differences in temperament. An excess of black bile supposedly caused a person to be gloomy and depressed. The Greeks called this supposed excess of black bile *melankholia* (*melan* "black" + *kholē* "bile").

Melankholia came to the Romans as *melancholia,* to the French as *melancolie,* and to the English (in the fourteenth century) as *malyncoly.* Since that time, *malyncoly* has been altered in spelling to *melancholy,* but its derivation has remained clear and its meaning intact. A sad, depressed person is still said to be *melancholy.*

PRE-TEST *In each group below, circle the letter of the word that is nearest in meaning to the word at the left. Then check your answers to see how you rate.*

1. **culpable**	(a) plausible	(b) praiseworthy	(c) blameworthy	(d) unbelievable
2. **manifest**	(a) conceal	(b) avert	(c) permit	(d) reveal
3. **recluse**	(a) disinclined	(b) sequestered	(c) gregarious	(d) judicious
4. **averse**	(a) loath	(b) heedless	(c) willing	(d) reckless
5. **retrospect**	(a) oblivion	(b) conviction	(c) recollection	(d) manifestation
6. **destitute**	(a) reluctant	(b) poor	(c) hesitant	(d) affluent
7. **specious**	(a) creditable	(b) incredible	(c) fair-seeming	(d) censurable
8. **perspicacious**	(a) opulent	(b) dense	(c) voluble	(d) discerning
9. **tenet**	(a) doctrine	(b) memory	(c) oblivion	(d) eremite
10. **circumspect**	(a) disinclined	(b) ostensible	(c) injudicious	(d) cautious
11. **preclude**	(a) demonstrate	(b) eliminate	(c) facilitate	(d) evidence
12. **loquacious**	(a) talkative	(b) taciturn	(c) sagacious	(d) deceptive

NUMBER CORRECT		RATING □ Extraordinary	□ Excellent	□ Good
		11–12 correct	9–10 correct	7–8 correct

55

1. averse	4. destitute	7. perspicacious	10. retrospect
2. circumspect	5. loquacious	8. preclude	11. specious
3. culpable	6. manifest	9. recluse	12. tenet

1. **a•verse′** (ə•vûrs′), *adj.* [From Latin *aversus* from *avertere: ab- (a-)* away from + *vertere* to turn.]
   Turned away in mind or feeling; opposed to.
   Although he was *averse* to the idea of having his wife work, it was necessary for a while.

   Synonyms: disinclined, hesitant, reluctant, loath
   Antonyms: inclined, eager, willing, favorable
   Related forms: aversion (n.), aversely (adv.)

2. **cir′cum•spect** (sûr′kum•spĕkt), *adj.* [From Latin *circumspectus* wary, cautious, from *circumspicere; circum-* around + *spicere* to look.]
   Showing caution; watchful on all sides; attentive to everything that may affect action or decision.
   When contemplating a ride down the steep and narrow trails of the Grand Canyon, one is especially anxious to procure a surefooted and *circumspect* mule.

   Synonyms: careful, cautious, wary; judicious, prudent, provident
   Antonyms: unwary, heedless, reckless; inattentive, injudicious, imprudent
   Related forms: circumspection (n.), circumspective (adj.), circumspectly (adv.), circumspectness (n.)

3. **cul′pa•ble** (kŭl′pə•b'l), *adj.* [From Latin *culpabilis* blameworthy, from *culpa* fault, blame.]
   Deserving blame.
   Not to know because of a neglect to study is *culpable* ignorance which will not go unpunished.

   Synonyms: blameworthy, censurable, reprehensible, reproachable
   Antonyms: praiseworthy, laudable, creditable, blameless, impeccable
   Related forms: culpability (n.), culpableness (n.), culpably (adv.)

4. **des′ti•tute** (dĕs′ti•tūt), *adj.* [From Latin *destitutis* abandoned, from *destituere: de-* away + *statuere* to place, to stand.]
   Deprived of the barest necessities of life; living in absolute poverty.
   Some people in America are poor, but the masses in India are *destitute.*

   Synonyms: poor, indigent, needy, penniless, poverty-stricken, necessitous
   Antonyms: opulent, rich, wealthy, affluent
   Related forms: destitute (n.), destitutely (adv.), destitution (n.)

5. **lo•qua′cious** (lō•kwā′shus), *adj.* [From Latin *loquax* talkative, from *loqui* to speak.]
   Very talkative.
   Our *loquacious* guide, obviously enjoying her work, chattered endlessly about even the most minute features of the historic mansion.

   Synonyms: garrulous, voluble, glib, prating, jabbering
   Antonyms: silent, reticent, taciturn, uncommunicative
   Related forms: loquaciously (adv.), loquaciousness (n.), loquacity (n.)

6. **man′i•fest** (măn′i•fĕst), *v.* [From Latin *manufestus* grasped by hand, from *manus* hand + *festus* gripped.]
   To reveal; to show plainly; to prove.
   "God was *manifest* in the flesh, justified in the Spirit, seen of angels, preached unto the Gentiles, believed on in the world, received up into glory." —*1 Tim. 3:16*

   Synonyms: show, evidence, evince, demonstrate
   Antonyms: conceal, mask, cover, hide
   Related forms: manifest (adj.), manifestable (adj.), manifestly (adv.), manifestation (n.), manifester (n.), manifestness (n.)

7. **per′spi•ca′cious** (pûr′spĭ•kā′sh*us*), *adj.* [From Latin *perspicax* sharp-sighted, from *perspicere: per-* through + *spicere* to see.]

   Having keen insight; mentally acute.

   > We must make allowance also for those blind spots which are found in the most *perspicacious* mortals. —*L. P. Smith*

   Synonyms: discerning, astute, shrewd, sagacious, perceptive
   Antonyms: dull, slow-witted, undiscerning, dumb, dense
   Related forms: perspicaciously (adv.), perspicaciousness (n.), perspicacity (n.)

8. **pre•clude′** (prĕ•klood′), *v.* [From Latin *praecludere: pre- (prae-)* before, in front + *claudere* to close.]

   To make impossible by previous action; eliminate.

   > The advent of winter with its heavy snows and frigid temperatures *precluded* Hitler's armies from defeating the Russians.

   Synonyms: forestall, prevent, avert, obviate, abort
   Antonyms: effect, facilitate, permit, further, promote, open the door for
   Related forms: preclusion (n.), preclusive (adj.)

9. **re•cluse′** (rĕ•kloos′; for *n.,* also rĕk′lūs), *n.* [From Latin *recludere* to close off: *re-* again + *claudere* to close.]

   n. ***One who withdraws from the world to live in seclusion.***

   > The old man was a castoff of society, a *recluse* who made his home in the mountain wilds.

   adj. ***Withdrawn from the world.***

   > Martin Luther thought that he could gain favor with God by living a *recluse* life in a monastery.

   Synonyms: hermit, eremite, anchorite, cenobite; sequestered, secluded, separated
   Antonyms: socializer; sociable, gregarious, neighborly, companionable
   Related forms: recluseness (n.), reclusion (n.), reclusive (adj.)

10. **ret′ro•spect** (rĕt′rō•spĕkt), *n.* [From Latin *retrospicere* to look back at: *retro-* back + *spicere* to look.]

    A looking back on the past; a review of something past.

    > My *retrospect* of life recalls to my view many opportunities of good neglected. —*Johnson*

    Synonyms: recollection, remembrance, memory, reminiscence
    Antonyms: forgetfulness, oblivion
    Related forms: retrospection (n.), retrospective (adj.)

11. **spe′cious** (spē′sh*us*), *adj.* [From Latin *speciosus* good-looking, beautiful, from *specere* to look at.]

    Apparently true or good but actually fallacious or insincere.

    > We all know what *specious* fallacies may be urged in defense of every act of injustice yet proposed for the imaginary benefit of the mass. —*Mill*

    Synonyms: plausible, ostensible, fair-seeming, deceptive
    Antonyms: genuine, valid; implausible, incredible, unbelievable
    Related forms: speciously (adv.), speciousness (n.)

    > *Man's natural instinct is never toward what is sound and true; it is toward what is specious and false.*
    > —*H. L. Mencken*

12. **ten′et** (tĕn′ĭt), *n.* [From Latin *tenet* he holds, from *tenere* to hold.]

    A belief, doctrine, or principle held as true.

    > Bible-believing Christians unabashedly defend the virgin birth of Christ as an essential *tenet* of the Christian faith.

    Synonyms: conviction, creed, precept, dogma

EXERCISE A *From the list of vocabulary words in this unit, choose the one that best completes each of the following sentences. Write the word in the blank provided.*

1. Although the oil-rich sheikdom of Kuwait has one of the world's highest Gross National Products, most of its people remain _____ **destitute** _____ .

2. A seemingly endless stream of questions poured forth from the _____ **loquacious** _____ three-year-old girl.

3. Christians are commanded to be _____ **circumspect** _____ , because "the devil, as a roaring lion, walketh about, seeking whom he may devour." —*1 Peter 5:8*

4. The Christian Scientists, founded by Mary Baker Eddy, are _____ **averse** _____ to any kind of medical help because they believe that sickness is unreal and can be overcome through proper spiritual understanding.

5. Because he was a(n) _____ **perspicacious** _____ reader of character, he did not take the young man's fulsome flattery seriously.

6. The sierra was so precipitous that it seemed to _____ **preclude** _____ all further progress. —*Prescott*

7. Multimillionaire Howard Hughes became a(n) _____ **recluse** _____ in 1950 and remained one until his death in 1976.

8. Seen in _____ **retrospect** _____ , many of the difficulties which we face will be revealed as priceless lessons from God.

9. Held prisoner by the Chinese, the missionaries were tempted by _____ **specious** _____ promises that they would be released if only they would confess to being American spies.

10. When asked by His disciples why a certain man had been blind from birth, Jesus answered: "Neither hath this man sinned, nor his parents: but that the works of God should be made _____ **manifest** _____ in him." —*John 9:3*

11. Under the _____ **tenets** _____ of socialism, all aspects of life are subject to political control.

12. The reckless bus driver showed a(n) _____ **culpable** _____ disregard for the safety of his passengers.

EXERCISE B *In each group below, circle the letter of the word that is either a **synonym** or an **antonym** of the word at the left.*

1. **averse**	(a) gregarious	(b) favorable	(c) impeccable	(d) laudable
2. **specious**	(a) prudent	(b) opulent	(c) wealthy	(d) genuine
3. **tenet**	(a) anchorite	(b) reclusion	(c) dogma	(d) memory
4. **culpable**	(a) cautious	(b) blameless	(c) sagacious	(d) gregarious
5. **loquacious**	(a) valid	(b) affluent	(c) laudable	(d) glib
6. **retrospect**	(a) forgetfulness	(b) conviction	(c) preclusion	(d) perspicacity
7. **circumspect**	(a) discerning	(b) reticent	(c) perceptive	(d) reckless
8. **manifest**	(a) permit	(b) obviate	(c) hide	(d) prevent
9. **preclude**	(a) conceal	(b) promote	(c) demonstrate	(d) evince
10. **destitute**	(a) necessitous	(b) plausible	(c) creditable	(d) prudent
11. **perspicacious**	(a) inattentive	(b) incredible	(c) slow-witted	(d) ostensible
12. **recluse**	(a) separated	(b) censurable	(c) disinclined	(d) reticent

EXERCISE C *Word Analysis.*

1. *Learn the meanings of the following word parts.*

Prefixes:

ante- before

circum- around

de- away, down, completely, negative

per- through, thoroughly

Roots:

CLUD, CLUS, CLOS to close

CULP blame, fault

LOQU, LOCUT to speak

MANU hand

SPEC, SPECT, SPIC to look, to see

ST(A), STAT, STIT to stand

TEN, TIN, TAIN to hold

VERT, VERS to turn

Suffixes:

-ast one who

-ety state, quality, act of

-ist one who

-mony state, quality, result of

2. *Using the Word Analyzer, write down the literal meaning of the following words. First, write the meanings of the various parts; next, rearrange the wording of the parts to formulate a good definition.*

irrevertible

in-[2] (ir-)	PREFIX	=	not
re-	PREFIX	=	back, again
VERT	ROOT	=	to turn
-ible	SUFFIX	=	able to (be)
	DEFINITION	=	not able to be turned back

circumspectly

circum	PREFIX	=	around
SPECT	ROOT	=	to look, to see
-ly[2]	SUFFIX	=	in the manner of
	DEFINITION	=	in the manner of looking around

exculpate

ex-	PREFIX	=	out (of), away from, without, intensive
CULP	ROOT	=	blame, fault
-ate[1]	SUFFIX	=	to make, to act, etc. (forms verbs)
	DEFINITION	=	to make without blame

Unit **8**

EXERCISE D *Verbal Analogies. In each of the following questions, a related pair of words or phrases is followed by five lettered pairs of words or phrases. Select the pair that best expresses a relationship similar to that expressed in the original pair. Circle the letter of your answer. [How to understand analogies is explained on pages x–xii.]*

1. HEART : BODY ::
  (a) moon : sun
  (b) horse: rider
  (c) water : pump
  (d) battery : car
  (e) bike : wheel

The *heart* helps one's *body* to function as a *battery* helps a *car* to run.

2. POLE : FISH ::
  (a) skin : fur
  (b) gun : deer
  (c) knife : steak
  (d) hunt : quail
  (e) trap : net

A *pole* is to a *fish* in fishing as a *gun* is to a *deer* in hunting.

3. CULPABLE : LAUDABLE ::
  (a) destitute : indigent
  (b) garrulous : voluble
  (c) hesitant : eager
  (d) manifest : demonstrate
  (e) facilitate : preclude

3. *Culpable* and *laudable* are both adjectives and are antonyms; *hesitant* and *eager* are both adjectives and are antonyms.

59

EXERCISE E   *Write an original sentence with each of the following words.*   **Answers will vary.**

1. averse _____

_____

_____

2. culpable _____

_____

_____

3. preclude _____

_____

_____

4. recluse _____

_____

_____

5. specious _____

_____

_____

Everyday Expressions

Ostracize

The word *ostracize* affords an interesting example of a figure of speech that has become embedded in the English language. We get it from the Greek *ostrakon,* "a tile or shell," because the votes inflicting the penalty of ostracism were inscribed on tiles or shells.

Ostracism means banishment or exclusion from social intercourse. In the ancient days in Greece it meant banishment for ten years, of such persons as were thought to be dangerous to the state. The votes were given by shells; each man marked upon his shell the name of the person he wished to banish. If the same name was upon the majority of 6,000 shells cast in Athens, the person was sentenced to banishment. The most upright and most distinguished citizens fell under this sentence; and the Athenians finally abolished it, as the Syracusans did a similar custom among them. Among the illustrious Athenians who were driven from the city by this custom of ostracism were Themistocles, Thucydides, Cimon, and Aristides.

UNIT 9

Harangue *(Word History)*

The word *harangue* has had a long and colorful history. It began its journey to us as a compound Germanic word *hring* "ring" and *hari* "host." This compound word spoke of a host of people standing in a ring to hear a public speech. The Italians borrowed the word and spelled it *aringo* meaning "a public place for assemblies and horse races." Their noun forms *aringa* and *arenga* meant "a public address." Their verb form *aringare* meant "to make a speech." Continuing its journey, this word traveled north to France, where it became *arenge* and *harangue*. It then crossed the English Channel and came to us as *harangue* meaning "a noisy or scolding public speech."

PRE-TEST *In each group below, circle the letter of the word that is nearest in meaning to the word at the left. Then check your answers to see how you rate.*

1. **dilettante**	(a) expert	(b) pedagogue	(c) amateur	(d) connoisseur
2. **motley**	(a) homogenous	(b) variegated	(c) haphazard	(d) meticulous
3. **ubiquitous**	(a) omnipresent	(b) scrupulous	(c) pernicious	(d) ostentatious
4. **baneful**	(a) desirable	(b) pernicious	(c) beneficial	(d) revolting
5. **pedant**	(a) novice	(b) connoisseur	(c) pedagogue	(d) dabbler
6. **fulsome**	(a) offensive	(b) admirable	(c) detrimental	(d) healthful
7. **punctilious**	(a) imprecise	(b) diverse	(c) uniform	(d) exact
8. **bureaucracy**	(a) ubiquity	(b) nonelective officials	(c) dilettantism	(d) pedantry
9. **garish**	(a) somber	(b) stoical	(c) slushy	(d) showy
10. **harangue**	(a) aspersion	(b) vindication	(c) defamation	(d) tirade
11. **calumny**	(a) praise	(b) oration	(c) slander	(d) declamation
12. **maudlin**	(a) sentimental	(b) phlegmatic	(c) ostentatious	(d) unemotional

NUMBER CORRECT ☐   **RATING** ☐ Extraordinary   ☐ Excellent   ☐ Good
                                     11–12 correct   9–10 correct   7–8 correct

Unit 9   Words from French, Italian, and English

1. baneful	4. dilettante	7. harangue	10. pedant
2. bureaucracy	5. fulsome	8. maudlin	11. punctilious
3. calumny	6. garish	9. motley	12. ubiquitous

1. **bane'ful** (bān'fŏŏl), *adj.* [From Old English *bana* murderer, destroyer.]
   Causing death, destruction, or ruin; very harmful.
   Since it is one of the most *baneful* and insidious of vices, griping should never be tolerated.

   Synonyms: pernicious, noxious, detrimental, toxic
   Antonyms: beneficial, profitable, healthful, wholesome
   Related forms: banefully (adv.), banefulness (n.)

2. **bu·reauc'ra·cy** (bŭ·rŏk'rə·sĭ), *n.* [From French *bureaucratie,* coined from French *bureau* desk, office + Greek *kratos* strength, power, rule.]
   Government through bureaus run by nonelective officials; government officials collectively.
   Note: This term is often applied to an administrative system in which the requirement of following complex procedures hinders effective action.
   It is not prudent to place power into the hands of those who are unaccountable to the people: *bureaucracy* inevitably tends to erode the freedoms for which Americans so bravely fought.

   Related forms: bureaucrat (n.), bureaucratic (adj.), bureaucratically (adv.), bureaucratize (v.), bureaucratization (n.)

3. **cal'um·ny** (kăl'*um*·nĭ), *n.* [From French *calomnie* and Latin *calumnia* trickery, false accusation, false report.]
   A false and malicious statement calculated to hurt someone's reputation.
   To seem disturbed at *calumny* is the way to make it believed, and stabbing your defamer will not prove you innocent. —*Blair*

   Synonyms: slander, libel, misrepresentation, defamation, aspersion
   Antonyms: eulogy, praise, laudation, vindication, compliment
   Related forms: calumnious (adj.), calumniation (n.), calumniator (n.), calumniate (v.)

4. **dil'et·tante'** (dĭl'*e*·tänt'; dĭl'*e*·tän'tĕ), *n.* [From Italian *dilettante* a lover of music or painting, from *dilettare* to delight, from Latin *delectare*.]
   A person who delights in an art or science in an amateurish or superficial way; a superficial amateur.
   The true poet is not . . . a mere artist living only for art, not a dreamer or a *dilettante,* sipping the nectar of existence, while he keeps aloof from its deeper interests. —*Shairp*

   Synonyms: dabbler, tyro, sciolist, nonprofessional, novice
   Antonyms: expert, professional, connoisseur, master
   Related forms: dilettante (adj.), dilettantism (n.), dilettantish (adj.)

5. **ful'some** (fŏŏl'*sum*), *adj.* [From Middle English *fulsom* abundant, disgustingly excessive: *ful* full + *som* some, but influenced in meaning by *ful* foul.]
   Disgusting or offensive, especially because excessive or insincere.
   The junior executive was discomfited in his attempt to gain advancement through *fulsome* praise of his employer.

   Synonyms: repulsive, revolting, nauseating, odious
   Antonyms: admirable, pleasing, desirable, agreeable
   Related forms: fulsomely (adv.), fulsomeness (n.)

6. **gar'ish** (gâr'ĭsh), *adj.* [The earlier spelling *gaurish* suggests a possible derivation from Middle English *gauren* to stare.]
   Too bright or glaring; showy.
   The *garish* costume of Caliban fascinated the children as they watched the performance of Shakespeare's *Tempest.*

   Synonyms: gaudy, tawdry, flashy, ostentatious
   Antonyms: somber, tasteful, subdued
   Related forms: garishly (adv.), garishness (n.)

7. **ha•rangue′** (hə•răng′), *n.* [Probably from Italian *aringare* from *aringo* a place of declamation, an arena.]

> ***A long, noisy, or scolding speech.***
>> Adolf Hitler used vehement *harangues* to inveigle the German people and gain support for his fateful policies.

> *Synonyms:* tirade, bombast, declamation, oration
> *Related forms:* haranguer (n.), harangue (v.)

8. **maud′lin** (môd′lĭn), *adj.* [From Middle English *Maudlin,* from Latin *Magdalena* alluding to the fact that painters used to represent Mary Magdalene with eyes red from weeping.]

> ***Tearfully or effusively sentimental.***
>> *Maudlin* sentiment is found in those parents who will not spank their children because they "love them too much."

> *Synonyms:* mawkish, romantic, slushy, emotional, weepy
> *Antonyms:* unemotional, composed, stoical, phlegmatic
> *Related forms:* maudlinly (adv.), maudlinness (n.)

9. **mot′ley** (mŏt′lĭ), *adj.* [From Middle English *mottely,* perhaps from Old English *mote* speck, spot.]
> ***Composed of various colors or elements.***
>> The pheasant, a bird of *motley* coloring, is a game bird often sought by hunters.

> *Synonyms:* variegated, parti-colored, checkered, dappled; heterogeneous, diverse, disparate
> *Antonyms:* unvariegated, colorless, monotone; homogeneous, uniform, alike

10. **ped′ant** (pĕd′ant), *n.* [From Italian *pedante* schoolmaster, probably ultimately from Greek *paidagogos* child leading: *paidos* child + *agogos* guide, leader.]

> ***One who makes an ostentatious display of knowledge; one who gives undue attention to trivial details of learning but has little interest in practical affairs.***
>> A man who has been brought up among books, and is able to talk of nothing else . . . is what we call a *pedant.* —*Addison*

> *Synonyms:* pedagogue, know-it-all (informal); quibbler, hairsplitter, pettifogger
> *Related forms:* pedantry (n.), pedantic (adj.)

Unit 9

11. **punc•til′i•ous** (pŭngk•tĭl′ĭ•us), *adj.* [From Italian *puntiglioso,* from Latin *punctum* a point.]
> ***Very attentive to every detail of etiquette or behavior; very exact.***
>> The *punctilious* hostess fretted over the inexperience of the waitresses who had been sent to serve at her elaborate dinner party.

> *Synonyms:* meticulous, scrupulous, particular, careful
> *Antonyms:* careless, neglectful, haphazard; imprecise, inexact
> *Related forms:* punctiliously (adv.), punctiliousness (n.), punctilio (n.)

12. **u•biq′ui•tous** (ŭ•bĭk′wĭ•tus), *adj.* [From French *ubiquité,* from Latin *ubique* everywhere: *ubi* where + *que* any.]
> ***Present or appearing everywhere at the same time.***
>> The *ubiquitous* American tourists, with their cameras and guide books, are an integral part of every European attraction.

> *Synonyms:* omnipresent, everywhere, universal
> *Related forms:* ubiquity (n.), ubiquitously (adv.), ubiquitousness (n.)

EXERCISE A *From the list of vocabulary words in this unit, choose the one that best completes each of the following sentences. Write the word in the blank provided.*

1. The king became disgusted with the _____fulsome_____ adulation of his chief adviser and dismissed him.

2. We endured the politicians' _____harangues_____ for two hours before getting up and leaving the convention.

3. The _____baneful_____ teachings of atheistic professors often destroy the beliefs of Christians who attend state universities.

4. No man can hide from the _____ubiquitous_____ eye of God.

5. Before C. T. Studd could leave for the mission field of China, he had to overcome the _____maudlin_____ sentiment of his family and friends.

6. The toucan, an unusual-looking bird found in the tropical forests of Central and South America, probably uses its large and often _____motley_____ bill to attract a mate.

7. _____Calumny_____ requires no proof. . . . To create an unfavorable impression, it is not necessary that certain things should be *true,* but that they *have been said.* —*Hazlitt*

8. The growth of the federal _____bureaucracy_____ in the United States has resulted in squandered resources and inefficient government.

9. Sporting a(n)_____garish_____ pierrot costume, the clown rode around the ring on a saddled ostrich.

10. Because many promising artists and musicians are averse to hard work, they remain _____dilettantes_____ rather than becoming masters.

11. The writings of Amy Vanderbilt and Emily Post are considered authoritative sources about how to maintain _____punctilious_____ social behavior.

12. The scholar, without good breeding, is a(n) _____pedant_____. —*Lord Chesterfield*

EXERCISE B *For each word in column **A**, select a word from column **B** that is most nearly a* **synonym** *of that word. Write its letter in the blank provided.*

	A		B
__l__	1. pedant	**a.**	novice
__g__	2. bureaucracy	**b.**	admirable
__n__	3. calumny	**c.**	dappled
__a__	4. dilettante	**d.**	bombast
__e__	5. baneful	**e.**	noxious
__d__	6. harangue	**f.**	meticulous
__i__	7. garish	**g.**	nonelective officials
__c__	8. motley	**h.**	universal
__k__	9. fulsome	**i.**	tawdry
__m__	10. maudlin	**j.**	unemotional
__h__	11. ubiquitous	**k.**	repulsive
__f__	12. punctilious	**l.**	hairsplitter
		m.	weepy
		n.	defamation

EXERCISE C *Word Analysis.*

1. *Learn the meanings of the following word parts.*

Prefixes:

apo- (ap-) away from, from
eu- good, well
para- (par-) beside, alongside
retro- backward, behind

Roots:

CHRON time
PHOT, PHOS light
PLAC to please, to appease
PORT to carry
REG, RECT to rule, to keeep straight
SENS, SENT to feel, to perceive
TANG, TACT, TING to touch
US, UT to use
VOLV, VOLU to roll, to turn, to wind

Suffixes:

-ar, -ary[1] like, pertaining to
-ar, -ary[2] one who
-ive[1] tending to, having the quality of
-ive[2] one who, that which

2. *Using the Word Analyzer, write down the literal meaning of the following words. First, write the meanings of the various parts; next, rearrange the wording of the parts to formulate a good definition.*

rectitude	RECT(I)	ROOT	=	to rule, to keep straight
	-tude	SUFFIX	=	state, quality, act of
		DEFINITION	=	quality of keeping straight
intangible	in-[2]	PREFIX	=	not
	TANG	ROOT	=	to touch
	-ible	SUFFIX	=	able to (be)
		DEFINITION	=	not able to be touched
implacability	in-[2] (im-)	PREFIX	=	not
	PLAC	ROOT	=	to please, to appease
	-able (-abil)	SUFFIX	=	able to (be)
	-ity	SUFFIX	=	state, quality, act of
		DEFINITION	=	quality of not being able to be appeased

EXERCISE D *Look up the word* careful *in* Webster's New Dictionary of Synonyms. *Under that word you will find discriminating explanations for the following words:* meticulous, scrupulous, *and* punctilious. *After studying these words, decide which of the three words best completes each of the following sentences.*

1. It's simply that I owe my city the most ____scrupulous____ performance of duty in safeguarding it from disease. —*Sinclair Lewis*

2. The more unpopular an opinion is, the more necessary is it that the holder should be somewhat ____punctilious____ in his observance of conventionalities generally. —*Samuel Butler*

3. The student took such ____meticulous____ care not to make any errors that he was the last one to finish the exam.

EXERCISE E   *Write an original sentence with each of the following words.*   **Answers will vary.**

1. baneful _____

_____

_____

2. fulsome _____

_____

_____

3. harangue _____

_____

_____

4. motley _____

_____

_____

5. punctilious _____

_____

_____

Unit
9

Everyday Expressions

Red Tape

Everybody has had experience, at one time or another, with "red tape," and its choking effect on business, public, and other. In a word, "red tape" means "formalism." Probably as good an example of the workings of "red tape" as any other is afforded by the following extract from an English magazine:

"There was an escape of gas at Cambridge Barracks, and this was the way of proceeding: The escape was discovered by a private, who reported it to his corporal; the corporal reported it to the color-sergeant, and the color sergeant to the quartermaster-sergeant.

"The quartermaster-sergeant had to report it to the quartermaster, and the quartermaster to the colonel commanding the regiment. The colonel had to report it to the commissariat officer in charge of the barracks, and the commissariat officer to the barrack-sergeant, who had to report it to the divisional officer of engineers. This officer had to report it to the district officer of engineers, and he to the clerk of works, Royal Engineers, who sends for a gasman to see if there is an escape, and report back again. While the reporting is going on, the barracks are burned down."

66

BULARY REVIEW 3
(Units 7–9)

EXERCISE A *In each group below, circle the letter of the word that is most nearly a* **synonym** *of the word at the left.*

1. **acrimonious** (a) dishonest (b) sarcastic (c) miserly (d) gracious
2. **salubrious** (a) courageous (b) wholesome (c) tightfisted (d) noxious
3. **loquacious** (a) taciturn (b) opulent (c) garrulous (d) reckless
4. **baneful** (a) admirable (b) repulsive (c) gaudy (d) detrimental
5. **harangue** (a) misrepresentation (b) recollection (c) declamation (d) eulogy
6. **mendacious** (a) irascible (b) surly (c) miserly (d) untruthful
7. **sedulous** (a) underhanded (b) busy (c) brusque (d) unoccupied
8. **retrospect** (a) remembrance (b) reclusion (c) vindication (d) oblivion
9. **maudlin** (a) niggardly (b) tasteful (c) emotional (d) phlegmatic
10. **dilettante** (a) anchorite (b) dabbler (c) bureaucrat (d) haranguer
11. **pedant** (a) nonprofessional (b) quibbler (c) calumniator (d) manifester
12. **ubiquitous** (a) everywhere (b) judicious (c) imprudent (d) creditable
13. **fulsome** (a) pleasing (b) ostentatious (c) revolting (d) unemotional
14. **manifest** (a) mask (b) permit (c) abort (d) show
15. **circumspect** (a) peevish (b) veracious (c) needy (d) careful
16. **propitious** (a) laudable (b) affluent (c) satisfied (d) beneficent
17. **garish** (a) flashy (b) romantic (c) voluble (d) uniform
18. **recluse** (a) hermit (b) socializer (c) expert (d) novice
19. **averse** (a) careful (b) reluctant (c) penniless (d) eager
20. **posthumous** (a) agreeable (b) fainthearted (c) wholesome (d) post-mortem

EXERCISE B *In each group below, circle the letter of the word that is most nearly an* **antonym** *of the word at the left.*

1. **mendacious** (a) caustic (b) honest (c) injurious (d) deceitful
2. **sedulous** (a) idle (b) busy (c) flattering (d) veracious
3. **manifest** (a) show (b) prevent (c) conceal (d) promote
4. **calumny** (a) memory (b) praise (c) pedantry (d) oration
5. **noxious** (a) wholesome (b) choleric (c) daring (d) openhanded
6. **pusillanimous** (a) mean-spirited (b) fretful (c) stouthearted (d) harmful
7. **surreptitious** (a) overt (b) deleterious (c) gruff (d) agreeable
8. **culpable** (a) reticent (b) reproachable (c) affluent (d) praiseworthy
9. **loquacious** (a) whining (b) needy (c) silent (d) discerning
10. **baneful** (a) subdued (b) variegated (c) detrimental (d) beneficial
11. **punctilious** (a) gaudy (b) careless (c) abrasive (d) scrupulous
12. **maudlin** (a) slushy (b) colorless (c) unemotional (d) somber
13. **retrospect** (a) aspersion (b) oblivion (c) precept (d) bombast
14. **circumspect** (a) careful (b) willing (c) odious (d) unwary
15. **propitious** (a) contrary (b) brave (c) industrious (d) secret

EXERCISE C   *In each group below, circle the letter of the word that is nearest in meaning to the expression in* **boldface type.**

1. wisely kept away from the **morally harmful** influence of society
    (a) mendacious   (b) noxious   (c) acrimonious   (d) unctuous

2. stood at the door, too **lacking in courage** to ring the doorbell
    (a) propitious   (b) querulous   (c) pusillanimous   (d) sedulous

3. **disgusting and offensive** greetings that evoked feelings of revulsion
    (a) specious   (b) fulsome   (c) loquacious   (d) acrimonious

4. dealt out allowances with a **stingy** hand
    (a) parsimonious   (b) surreptitious   (c) pusillanimous   (d) mendacious

5. because the **mentally acute** counselor gave good advice
    (a) perspicacious   (b) parsimonious   (c) circumspect   (d) propitious

6. a **superficial amateur,** having only a cursory acquaintance with the works of the baroque masters
    (a) pedant   (b) recluse   (c) calumniator   (d) dilettante

7. no reason to be **full of complaints** and discontent
    (a) querulous   (b) salubrious   (c) noxious   (d) averse

8. approached his customers with an **insincerely suave** smile
    (a) acrimonious   (b) unctuous   (c) averse   (d) inauspicious

9. could not condone such **deserving blame** negligence
    (a) garish   (b) baneful   (c) culpable   (d) fulsome

10. spending too much time in **looking back on the past**
    (a) circumspection   (b) calumny   (c) retrospect   (d) perspicacity

Units
7–9

11. having become **deprived of the barest necessities of life** and all alone in the world
    (a) destitute   (b) posthumous   (c) maudlin   (d) parsimonious

12. held tenaciously to the **beliefs, doctrines, or principles** of orthodoxy
    (a) pedantries   (b) tenets   (c) ubiquities   (d) harangues

13. can **eliminate** misunderstandings by giving clear, specific instructions in advance
    (a) preclude   (b) mask   (c) manifest   (d) evince

14. good men unable to escape the **false and malicious statements** of inferior men
    (a) harangues   (b) tenets   (c) calumnies   (d) acrimony

15. a **too bright or glaring** outfit of plaid trousers, striped shirt, pink jacket, and bright yellow shoes
    (a) maudlin   (b) garish   (c) specious   (d) fulsome

16. food giveaways attracted a **composed of various elements** crowd
    (a) destitute   (b) propitious   (c) parsimonious   (d) motley

17. **apparently true or good but actually fallacious or insincere** declarations of Soviet propagandists
    (a) mendacious   (b) unctuous   (c) fulsome   (d) specious

18. were not fooled by the **long, noisy, scolding speeches** of the demagogue
    (a) calumnies   (b) circumspections   (c) harangues   (d) punctilios

19. the **very exact** attention to protocol in diplomatic circles
    (a) circumspect   (b) punctilious   (c) sedulous   (d) fulsome

20. the **unauthorized** reading of another's private mail
    (a) posthumous   (b) circumspect   (c) culpable   (d) surreptitious

EXERCISE D *From the following list of vocabulary words, choose the one that best completes each of the following sentences. Write the word in the blank provided.*

acrimonious	destitute	perspicacious	querulous	tenet
averse	motley	posthumous	salubrious	ubiquitous
bureaucracy	parsimonious	preclude	specious	unctuous

1. The more _____perspicacious_____ members could easily see the hidden purpose behind this seemingly honest proposal. —*Ayers*

2. The Vietnam War left thousands of Vietnamese _____destitute_____ and seeking refuge.

3. The businessman was _____averse_____ to any form of slothfulness, and had an office full of alert, busy workers to prove it.

4. The Germanic tribes made the Celts a(n) _____specious_____ offer to protect them from their enemies, but they themselves were really intending to take over the Celts' land.

5. The lame man did not need the _____salubrious_____ effects of the pool of Bethesda when Jesus was there to heal him.

6. They were saddened to see their aged grandmother, who had always been cheerful and content, become grumpy and _____querulous_____ .

7. A violent thunderstorm _____precluded_____ any possibility of our having our annual Fourth of July picnic.

Units
7–9

8. The monstrous federal _____bureaucracy_____ in the United States employs nearly three million civilians.

9. The _____ubiquitous_____ peddlers, hawking their wares, swarmed around our tour bus at every stop.

10. He [Ben Johnson] . . . was _____posthumous_____, being born a month after his father's death.

—*William Drummond*

11. In the *Adventures of Huckleberry Finn*, the _____unctuous_____ manner of the "King" enabled him to fleece a few hundred dollars from unwary men who attended his theatrical performance.

12. The law of supply and demand is one of the main _____tenets_____ of capitalism.

13. Political hostility had been embittered by the most _____acrimonious_____ disputes. —*May*

14. Her expenditure was _____parsimonious_____ and even miserly. —*Green*

15. In . . . Singapore, we see a(n) _____motley_____ population attracted from China, the Malay Peninsula, and India. —*Lubbock*

> *The world is naturally averse*
> *To all truth it sees or hears,*
> *But swallows nonsense and a lie*
> *With greediness and gluttony.* —*Samuel Butler*

EXERCISE E *In each of the following analogies, a related pair of words or phrases is followed by five lettered pairs of words or phrases. Select the pair that best expresses a relationship similar to that expressed in the original pair. Circle the letter of your answer.*

1. HEEDLESS : CIRCUMSPECT ::
   (a) destitute : indigent
   (b) loquacious : voluble
   (c) show : demonstrate
   (d) retrospect : oblivion
   (e) conviction : precept
   (n : n; ant.)

2. PUNCTILIOUSLY : PUNCTILIO ::
   (a) ubiquitously : ubiquity
   (b) bureaucrat : bureaucratic
   (c) dilettantish : novice
   (d) baneful : banefully
   (e) calumniate : defamation
   (adv : n; rel.)

3. NOXIOUS : SALUBRIOUS ::
   (a) propitious : agreeable
   (b) penurious : lavish
   (c) querulous : peevish
   (d) covert : furtive
   (e) greasy : unctuous
   (adj : adj; ant.)

4. CALUMNY : PRAISE ::
   (a) garish : tasteful
   (b) motley : monotone
   (c) pedant : quibbler
   (d) sciolist : expert
   (e) admirable : pleasing
   (n : n; ant.)

5. CAUSTIC : ACRIMONIOUS ::
   (a) mendacious : veracious
   (b) fainthearted : daring
   (c) parsimonious : niggardly
   (d) salubrious : noxious
   (e) busy : lazy
   (adj : adj; syn.)

6. MANIFEST : EVINCE ::
   (a) astute : dense
   (b) tenet : dogma
   (c) averse : favorable
   (d) recluse : socializer
   (e) facilitate : preclude
   (n : n; syn.)

EXERCISE F *Match each prefix, root, or suffix in column **A** with its definition in column **B**. Some definitions may be used more than once.*

Units 7–9

	A		B
o	1. -ory², orium	a.	sound, voice
t	2. eu-	b.	to carry
b	3. PORT	c.	to close
y	4. CERN, CRET	d.	same
l	5. VERT, VERS	e.	under
m	6. post-	f.	hand
g	7. ST(A), STAT, STIT	g.	to stand
w	8. CULP	h.	through, thoroughly
s	9. FORT	i.	able to (be)
z	10. retro-	j.	beside, alongside
n	11. CHRON	k.	one who
k	12. -ist	l.	to turn
v	13. TANG, TACT, TING	m.	after
h	14. per-	n.	time
c	15. CLUD, CLUS, CLOS	o.	place where, thing which
a	16. PHON	p.	before
e	17. sub-	q.	state, quality, act of
w	18. PLAC	r.	to snatch, to seize
q	19. -ety	s.	strong
x	20. VOLV, VOLU	t.	good, well
p	21. ante-	u.	to please, to appease
r	22. RAP, RAPT	v.	to touch
k	23. -ast	w.	blame, fault
f	24. MANU	x.	to roll, to turn, to wind
j	25. para-	y.	to separate, to distinguish
		z.	backward, behind

EXERCISE G *Word Analysis. The following words contain prefixes, roots, and suffixes that you have memorized. Write down from memory the literal meaning of these words. Write the meanings of the various parts; rearrange the wording of the parts as necessary to formulate a good definition.*

euphonious	eu-	PREFIX	=	**good, well**
	PHON	ROOT	=	**sound, voice**
	-(i)ous	SUFFIX	=	**having the quality of**
		DEFINITION	=	**having the quality of good sound**
loquacious	LOQU(AC)	ROOT	=	**to speak**
	-(i)ous	SUFFIX	=	**having the quality of**
		DEFINITION	=	**having the quality of speaking**
retrovert	retro-	PREFIX	=	**backward, behind**
	VERT	ROOT	=	**to turn**
		DEFINITION	=	**to turn backward**
perspicuous	per-	PREFIX	=	**through, thoroughly**
	SPIC	ROOT	=	**to look, to see**
	-(u)ous	SUFFIX	=	**having the quality of**
		DEFINITION	=	**having the quality of being seen through**
circumvolutory	circum-	PREFIX	=	**around**
	VOLU(T)	ROOT	=	**to roll, to turn, to wind**
	-ory[1]	SUFFIX	=	**like, pertaining to**
		DEFINITION	=	**pertaining to winding around**

Units 7–9

Everyday Expressions

Clincher

"That's a 'clincher,' " says a man listening to a political speech; "you can't get around that argument." And that is exactly what a "clincher" is—something that you cannot get around, something that ends or settles an argument or a controversy.

The dictionary does not cast any light on the origin of the term, but it is said to have had its rise in the following story:

Two notorious liars were matched against each other, to see which of the two could tell the bigger "whopper." The first one said, "I drove a nail through the moon once." To this the other replied, "Yes, that's true; I remember the circumstance well, because I went around to the back and clinched it."

UNIT 10

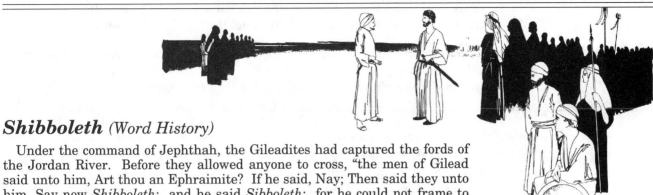

Shibboleth (Word History)

Under the command of Jephthah, the Gileadites had captured the fords of the Jordan River. Before they allowed anyone to cross, "the men of Gilead said unto him, Art thou an Ephraimite? If he said, Nay; Then said they unto him, Say now *Shibboleth:* and he said *Sibboleth:* for he could not frame to pronounce it right. Then they took him, and slew him at the passages of Jordan" (Judges 12:5, 6).

Because the Ephraimites could not pronounce the *sh* sound, the Gileadites employed *shibboleth* as a test word to identify the enemy. From this clever ruse, we adopted the present meaning of *shibboleth:* a password or phrase that readily differentiates one group of people from another.

During World War II, Americans used *shibboleths* to expose the Japanese who, by posing as friendly Filipinos, were infiltrating Allied lines. Because the Japanese could not pronounce the letter *l,* they pronounced *shibboleths* such as *lallapaloosa* as *rarraparoosa,* which was the last mistake they ever made.

PRE-TEST *In each group below, circle the letter of the word that is nearest in meaning to the word at the left. Then check your answers to see how you rate.*

1. **forensic**   (a) rustic   (b) argumentative   (c) refined   (d) innate

2. **nocturnal**   (a) celestial   (b) rudimentary   (c) daily   (d) nightly

3. **intrinsic**   (a) theatrical   (b) inherent   (c) despondent   (d) undisturbed

4. **puerile**   (a) childish   (b) mature   (c) cultured   (d) unprofitable

5. **bucolic**   (a) rural   (b) asinine   (c) urban   (d) civil

6. **sanguine**   (a) pessimistic   (b) simple   (c) cheerful   (d) explosive

7. **mundane**   (a) gainless   (b) worldly   (c) heavenly   (d) diurnal

8. **histrionic**   (a) natural   (b) predictable   (c) melodramatic   (d) grown-up

9. **secular**   (a) nonreligious   (b) unaffected   (c) capricious   (d) divine

10. **lucrative**   (a) pale   (b) profitable   (c) worthless   (d) extrinsic

11. **volatile**   (a) artificial   (b) stable   (c) argumentative   (d) changeful

12. **incipient**   (a) terminating   (b) doubtful   (c) initial   (d) foreign

NUMBER CORRECT [ ]   **RATING** □ Extraordinary   □ Excellent   □ Good
                                       11–12 correct   9–10 correct   7–8 correct

Unit
10

1. **bucolic**	4. **incipient**	7. **mundane**	10. **sanguine**
2. **forensic**	5. **intrinsic**	8. **nocturnal**	11. **secular**
3. **histrionic**	6. **lucrative**	9. **puerile**	12. **volatile**

1. **bu•col′ic** (bŭ•kŏl′ĭk), *adj.* [From Latin *bucolicus,* from Greek *boukolikos* of herdsmen, from *boukolos* herdsmen: *bous* ox, cow + *kolos* keeper.]

   Of or pertaining to shepherds or herdsmen; pertaining to country life or country people.

   > Thomas Gray in his *bucolic* poem "Elegy Written in a Country Churchyard" glorified the graves of villagers in the familiar lines "Full many a flower is born to blush unseen, / And waste its sweetness on the desert air."

   Synonyms: pastoral, rural, rustic, simple
   Antonyms: urban, urbane, refined, cultured
   Related forms: bucolical (adj.), bucolically (adv.), bucolic (n.)

2. **fo•ren′sic** (fŏ•rĕn′sĭk), *adj.* [From Latin *forensis* pertaining to the forum.]
   Pertaining to law courts or formal argumentation.

   > The experienced lawyer's *forensic* eloquence gave him a decided advantage over the tyro who opposed him.

   Synonyms: litigious, argumentative, debatable, rhetorical
   Related forms: forensics (n.), forensically (adv.)

3. **his′tri•on′ic** (hĭs′trĭ•ŏn′ĭk), *adj.* [From Latin *histrionicus* pertaining to an actor, from *histrio* actor, which is of Etruscan origin.]
   Pertaining to actors or acting; overly dramatic, affected.

   > The *histrionic* performance did not convey the true emotion and drama of the play.

   Synonyms: dramatic, theatrical, melodramatic, artificial
   Antonyms: natural, unaffected, artless
   Related forms: histrionical (adj.), histrionically (adv.) histrionism (n.), histrionics (n.)

4. **in•cip′i•ent** (ĭn•sĭp′ĭ•ent), *adj.* [From Latin *incipere* to begin.]
   Just beginning to exist or appear.

   > When the dove sent forth by Noah returned to the ark with an olive leaf, Noah knew that there was *incipient* plant life where the waters had subsided.

   Synonyms: initial, commencing, embryonic, inaugural, rudimentary
   Antonyms: terminating, ending, expiring, ceasing
   Related forms: incipiently (adv.), incipience (n.), incipiency (n.)

5. **in•trin′sic** (ĭn•trĭn′sĭk), *adj.* [From Latin *intrinsecus* on the inside: *intra-* within + *secus* close, following.]
   Pertaining to the real nature of a thing; inherent.

   > To many people, humanistic philosophy seems innocuous; but to perceptive observers its *intrinsic* evil is apparent.

   Synonyms: ingrained, constitutional, innate, congenital, inborn
   Antonyms: extrinsic, uninherent, extraneous, foreign, alien
   Related form: intrinsically (adv.)

6. **lu′cra•tive** (lū′krə•tĭv), *adj.* [From Latin *lucrativus,* from *lucrari* to profit.]
   Producing gain or wealth; profitable.

   > Within a year after arriving in America, the ingenious young immigrant had established a *lucrative* business.

   Synonyms: gainful, profit-making, moneymaking, well-paying, remunerative
   Antonyms: unprofitable, gainless, unpaying, worthless
   Related forms: lucratively (adv.), lucrativeness (n.)

7. **mun′dane** (mŭn′dān), *adj.* [From Latin *mundanus* of or pertaining to the world, from *mundus* world.]
   Pertaining to the world; worldly as opposed to the spiritual and eternal.

   We should not get so caught up in the *mundane* affairs of this life that we forget we are created for eternity.

   Synonyms: worldly, earthly, terrestrial, material, temporal
   Antonyms: heavenly, celestial; eternal, infinite
   Related forms: mundanely (adv.), mundaneness (n.)

8. **noc•tur′nal** (nŏk•tûr′nal), *adj.* [From Latin *nocturnus,* from *nox* night.]
   Pertaining to the night; done or occurring in the night.

   The eyes of most fish are adapted to the conditions of dim illumination associated with *nocturnal* feeding. —*Dowdeswell*

   Synonyms: nightly, nighttime
   Antonyms: diurnal, daily, daytime
   Related forms: nocturne (n.), nocturnal (n.), nocturnally (adv.)

9. **pu′er•ile** (pū′ĕr•ĭl; pū′ĕr•īl), *adj.* [From Latin *puerilis* boyish, childish, from *puer* a boy, child.]
   Characteristic of a child; childishly foolish, trifling.

   His first attempts at writing expository prose were inadequate and *puerile,* but through much practice and close application of sound writing principles, he has become a well-known writer for a prominent magazine.

   Synonyms: childish, immature, juvenile; asinine, trivial
   Antonyms: adult, mature, grown-up; significant
   Related forms: puerilely (adv.), puerility (n.)

10. **san′guine** (săng′gwĭn), *adj.* [From Latin *sanguineus* of blood, blood red, from *sanguis* blood.]
    Of the color of blood, ruddy; cheerful, hopeful.

    The work was pushed to completion under difficulties that might have killed a person of less *sanguine* temperament.

    Synonyms: rosy-cheeked; assured, confident, optimistic, lighthearted
    Antonyms: pale; pessimistic, doubtful, despondent
    Related forms: sanguinely (adv.), sanguiness (n.), sanguineous (adj.)

> *If . . . England expects every man to do his duty, England is the most sanguine country on the face of the earth, and will find itself continually disappointed.* —*Charles Dickens*

Unit 10

11. **sec′u•lar** (sĕk′û•lẽr), *adj.* [From Latin *saecularis* of an age, from *saeculum* an age, generation.]
    Not pertaining to church or religion; worldly.

    The *secular* philosophies of our day dominate most state universities.

    Synonyms: nonspiritual, temporal, nonreligious, civil
    Antonyms: religious, sacred, spiritual, divine
    Related forms: secularism (n.), secularist (n., adj.), secularly (adv.), secularize (v.), secularistic (adj.)

12. **vol′a•tile** (vŏl′ə•tĭl; -tīl), *adj.* [From Latin *volatilis* flying, fleeting, from *volare* to fly.]
    Changing unpredictably; tending to break out into violence.

    Because of the *volatile* conditions in the Middle East, American tourists are not allowed to visit certain areas.

    Synonyms: changeful, capricious, mercurial; explosive, eruptive, charged
    Antonyms: stable, invariable, predictable; tranquil, imperturbable, undisturbed
    Related forms: volatility (n.), volatileness (n.), volatilize (v.)

EXERCISE A *From the list of vocabulary words in this unit, choose the one that best completes each of the following sentences. Write the word in the blank provided.*

1. The _____forensic_____ club met to discuss the upcoming high school debate.

2. When the subject has no _____intrinsic_____ dignity, it must necessarily owe its attractions to artificial embellishments. —*Johnson*

3. His _____sanguine_____ personality caused those around him to be more optimistic and cheerful.

4. The squares of light along the fifteenth story testified until midnight of their _____nocturnal_____ industry. —*Auchincloss*

5. Even though his writing is _____secular_____ , it is in line with Christian ethics.

6. Ephesians 4:14 encourages us not to be _____puerile_____ in our thinking, "tossed to and fro, and carried about with every wind of doctrine."

7. Hard work and ingenuity had won the young man a(n) _____lucrative_____ managerial position.

8. The angry and _____volatile_____ situation in Northern Ireland between Catholics and Protestants seems destined to remain unresolved.

9. The actress's _____histrionic_____ weeping was so overdone that the audience laughed at her plight.

10. The psychological analyses, casuistical questions, rhetorical digressions, and pathetic situations . . . were exactly suited to the intellectual tastes and temper of _____incipient_____ decadence.
    —*Symonds*

11. In the thick of traffic, shepherds pass along with_____bucolic_____ slowness and serenity, clad in clothes like those worn by their ancestors. —*Atlantic Monthly*

12. Tony knew that she did not allow them to talk of _____mundane_____ affairs on these expeditions to and from church. —*Archibald Marshall*

EXERCISE B *For each word in column **A**, select a word from column **B** that is is most nearly a* **synonym** *of that word. Write its letter in the blank provided.*

A		B
m	1. forensic	a. refined
h	2. nocturnal	b. earthly
j	3. sanguine	c. dramatic
c	4. histrionic	d. civil
f	5. volatile	e. well-paying
e	6. lucrative	f. eruptive
n	7. bucolic	g. unaffected
l	8. puerile	h. nighttime
k	9. intrinsic	i. commencing
b	10. mundane	j. confident
d	11. secular	k. innate
i	12. incipient	l. juvenile
		m. litigious
		n. pastoral

EXERCISE C *Word Analysis.*

1. *Learn the meanings of the following word parts.*

Prefixes:	**Roots:**	**Suffixes:**
ambi-, amphi- both, around	AUDI to hear	***-al, -an,*** [1] ***-ane*** like, pertaining to
extra- outside, beyond	CIDE, CIS to kill, to cut	***-an*** [2] one who
intro-, intra- inside, within	DUC, DUCT to lead	***-ic, -ical*** like, pertaining to
meta- (met-) along with, after, beyond, change	FRANG, FRACT, FRING to break	***-id, -ile, -ine, -ish*** like, pertaining to
	GRAT free, pleasing, grateful	
	NEO new	
	PON, POS(IT), POUND to place, to put	
	VER true	
	VOC, VOK voice, to call	

2. *Using the Word Analyzer, write down the literal meaning of the following words. First, write the meanings of the various parts; next, rearrange the wording of the parts to formulate a good definition.*

interposition	inter-	PREFIX	=	between, among
	POS(IT)	ROOT	=	to place, to put
	-ion	SUFFIX	=	state, quality, act of, -ing
		DEFINITION	=	act of placing between
inaudible	in-[2]	PREFIX	=	not
	AUD(I)	ROOT	=	to hear
	-ible	SUFFIX	=	able to (be)
		DEFINITION	=	not able to be heard
introductory	intro-	PREFIX	=	inside, within
	DUCT	ROOT	=	to lead
	-ory[1]	SUFFIX	=	like, pertaining to
		DEFINITION	=	pertaining to leading within (inside)

Unit 10

EXERCISE D *For each of the following words, list the antonyms given in this lesson.*

1. bucolic   urban, urbane, refined, cultured

2. histrionic   natural, unaffected, artless

3. incipient   terminating, ending, expiring, ceasing

4. mundane   heavenly, celestial; eternal, infinite

5. secular   religious, sacred, spiritual, divine

EXERCISE E   *Write an original sentence with each of the following words.*   Answers will vary.

1. forensic _____

    _____

    _____

2. intrinsic _____

    _____

    _____

3. puerile _____

    _____

    _____

4. sanguine _____

    _____

    _____

5. volatile _____

    _____

    _____

Everyday Expressions

Utopia

"Utopia" is the name of an imaginary island, the scene of Sir Thomas More's romance of the "Happy Republic." According to the author, the island was discovered by a companion of Amerigo Vespucci, after whom America was named. Utopia was the abode of a happy society, which, by virtue of its wise organization and legislation, was wholly free from the harassing cares, inordinate and greedy desires, and attendant customary miseries of mankind.

In Utopia there is no greed, no passion, no malice, no hatred, and everyone is perfectly happy. However, it is to be borne in mind that Sir Thomas More formed the name from two Greek words "ou," meaning "not," and "topos," meaning "place"—in other words, "Utopia" means "nowhere."

"Utopian" schemes or plans are those that cannot possibly be brought to realization.

UNIT 11

Allegory (Word History)

The word *allegory* is derived from the Greek words *allos,* meaning "something else," and *agoria,* meaning "a discourse." Athenians often used *allegories* when criticizing public officials in order to minimize the risk of political reprisals. Although the speaker veiled his criticism in a fictitious story, he made certain that his audience could understand his allusions. In Grecian times, the spoken *allegory* was prevalent, but today most *allegories* appear in written form. Perhaps the most familiar allegory is the excellent Christian allegory *Pilgrim's Progress* by John Bunyan. Next time you read an *allegory,* look for the "discourse" on "something else."

PRE-TEST *In each group below, circle the letter of the word that is nearest in meaning to the word at the left. Then check your answers to see how you rate.*

1. **derogatory**	(a) villainous	(b) praising	(c) rambling	(d) belittling
2. **nebulous**	(a) sinuous	(b) jovial	(c) detracting	(d) clouded
3. **abstruse**	(a) principled	(b) extensive	(c) obscure	(d) direct
4. **scrupulous**	(a) grave	(b) dishonest	(c) conscientious	(d) silly
5. **fatuous**	(a) foolish	(b) distinct	(c) meticulous	(d) godly
6. **variegated**	(a) uniform	(b) sedate	(c) parti-colored	(d) sparse
7. **circuitous**	(a) profuse	(b) indirect	(c) muddled	(d) degenerate
8. **nefarious**	(a) wicked	(b) motley	(c) unprincipled	(d) garrulous
9. **lugubrious**	(a) glad	(b) hazy	(c) mournful	(d) sensible
10. **copious**	(a) plentiful	(b) vacuous	(c) slighting	(d) plain
11. **taciturn**	(a) lighthearted	(b) silent	(c) serpentine	(d) righteous
12. **facetious**	(a) pejorative	(b) ethical	(c) joking	(d) reserved

Unit
11

NUMBER CORRECT ☐   **RATING** ☐ Extraordinary   ☐ Excellent   ☐ Good
11–12 correct   9–10 correct   7–8 correct

1. abstruse	4. derogatory	7. lugubrious	10. scrupulous
2. circuitous	5. facetious	8. nebulous	11. taciturn
3. copious	6. fatuous	9. nefarious	12. variegated

1. **ab•struse′** (āb•strōos′), *adj.* [From Latin *abstrusus* thrust away, concealed, from *abstrudere: abs-* (*ab-*) away + *trudere* to thrust.]
    Difficult to understand; obscure.
    > Unless one has an analytical mind, he may find higher mathematics courses to be *abstruse*.

    Synonyms: abstract, recondite, profound, deep
    Antonyms: obvious, plain, intelligible, perspicuous
    Related forms: abstrusely (adv.), abstruseness (n.)

2. **cir•cu′i •tous** (sĕr•kū′*i*•t*us*), *adj.* [From Latin *circuitus* a going round.]
    Taking a roundabout course; indirect.
    > The flooding in Louisiana caused travelers in that area to take a rather *circuitous* route.

    Synonyms: tortuous, sinuous, serpentine, winding, rambling, devious
    Antonyms: straight, direct, uncurved, forthright, straightforward
    Related forms: circuitously (adv.), circuitousness (n.), circuity (n.)

3. **co′pi•ous** (kō′pĭ•*us*), *adj.* [From Latin *copiosus* abounding, plentiful, from *copia* plenty.]
    Yielding or containing plenty (of information, thoughts, vocabulary).
    > You have two or three of my letters to answer, and I hope you will be *copious* and distinct, and tell me a great deal of your mind. —*Samuel Johnson*

    Synonyms: plentiful, extensive, profuse, abundant
    Antonyms: meager, scanty, sparse, exiguous
    Related forms: copiously (adv.), copiousness (n.)

4. **de•rog′a•to′ry** (dĕ•rŏg′ə•tō′rĭ), *adj.* [From Latin *derogatorius,* from *derogare* to take away, diminish: *de-* away + *rogare* to ask.]
    Tending to detract, as from authority or estimation; disparaging.
    > Some people make *derogatory* remarks about others in order to make themselves appear more virtuous.

    Synonyms: depreciatory, slighting, pejorative, belittling, detracting
    Antonyms: approbatory, commendatory, praising, honoring, overestimating
    Related forms: derogatorily (adv.), derogation (n.), derogative (adj.), derogator (n.), derogate (v.)

5. **fa•ce′tious** (fə•sē′sh*us*), *adj.* [From Latin *facetia* jest, witticism, from *facetus* elegant, witty.]
    Joking; usually clumsy or inappropriate joking.
    > The *facetious* remarks of the speaker at the dedication service embarrassed the others on the platform.

    Synonyms: humorous, waggish, droll, jocular
    Antonyms: lugubrious, serious, grave, sedate
    Related forms: facetiously (adv.), facetiousness (n.)

6. **fat′u•ous** (făt′ū•*us*), *adj.* [From Latin *fatuus* foolish, silly.]
    Characterized by foolishness, stupidity, and inanity.
    > She still engaged in those *fatuous remarks* that had no point. Remarks like: Marriage is an institution made chiefly for men and women. —*Abse*

    Synonyms: simple, foolish, silly, inane, vacuous
    Antonyms: sensible, wise, prudent, judicious
    Related forms: fatuously (adv.), fatuousness (n.), fatuity (n.)

7. **lu·gu′bri·ous** (lŭ·gū′brĭ·*us*), *adj.* [From Latin *lugubris* from *lugere* to mourn, lament.]
   Mournful, especially to an exaggerated degree.
   > The only evident reason for Roderick Usher's *lugubrious* behavior was the impending death of his sister, Madeline.

   Synonyms: doleful, rueful, melancholy, dolorous, cheerless
   Antonyms: joyous, glad, cheerful, lighthearted, jovial
   Related forms: lugubriously (adv.), lugubriousness (n.)

8. **neb′u·lous** (nĕb′ū·l*us*), *adj.* [From Latin *nebulosus* cloudy, from *nebula* cloud.]
   Clouded; vague; indistinct.
   > One who writes in a *nebulous* style, rather than by using specific and concrete words, is either snobbish or fuzzy headed; but at any rate he is a menace to clear communication.

   Synonyms: obscure, hazy, muddled, abstract, nonspecific
   Antonyms: clear, lucid, concrete, distinct, well-defined
   Related forms: nebulously (adv.), nebulousness (n.), nebulosity (n.)

9. **ne·far′i·ous** (nĕ·fâr′ĭ·*us*), *adj.* [From Latin *nefarius* from *nefas* crime, wrong: *ne-* not + *fas* lawful.]
   Extremely wicked.
   > The same person who weeps over a dying dog is often callous to the *nefarious* practice of abortion.

   Synonyms: iniquitous, corrupt, degenerate, vicious, villainous, vile
   Antonyms: virtuous, moral, ethical, righteous, noble, godly
   Related forms: nefariously (adv.), nefariousness (n.)

> *Let wickedness escape, as it may at the bar, it never fails of doing justice upon itself; for every guilty person is his own hangman.*　　　　　　　*—Seneca*

---

10. **scru′pu·lous** (skroo′pŭ·l*us*), *adj.* [From Latin *scrupulus* small, sharp stone. (When such a stone falls into a person's shoe it causes the person to pay attention to the stone even though it is a small particular.)]
    Very conscientious; extremely thorough; closely attentive to what is right and proper.
    > We should be religiously *scrupulous* and exact to say nothing . . . but what is true. —*Butler*

    Synonyms: meticulous, punctilious, careful; upright, honest, principled
    Antonyms: remiss, negligent, neglectful; unprincipled, dishonest, unethical
    Related forms: scrupulously (adv.), scrupulousness (n.), scrupulosity (n.), scruple (n.), scrupulist (n.), scrupler (n.)

11. **tac′i·turn** (tăs′*i*·tûrn), *adj.* [From Latin *taciturnus,* from *tacitus* silent, from *tacere* to be silent.]
    Habitually silent; not liking to talk.
    > The farmer was *taciturn* and drove them speechlessly to the house. —*Buck*

    Synonyms: silent, uncommunicative, reserved, reticent
    Antonyms: garrulous, conversational, unreserved, effusive
    Related forms: taciturnly (adv.), taciturnist (n.), taciturnity (n.)

Unit 11

12. **var′i·e·gat′ed** (vâr′i·e·gāt′ed; -ĭd), *adj.* [From Late Latin *variegare* to make of various colors, from *varius* changing + *agere* to set in motion.]
    Having different colors in streaks, spots, or patches; characterized by variety.
    > The *variegated* tulips, spreading a swath of color over the campus, announced the coming of spring.

    Synonyms: parti-colored, motley, checkered, dappled, pied, piebald, skewbald
    Antonyms: uniform, unvaried, unvariegated
    Related forms: variegatedness (n.), variegation (n.), variegate (v.)

EXERCISE A *From the list of vocabulary words in this unit, choose the one that best completes each of the following sentences. Write the word in the blank provided.*

1. Probably the most tedious bore on earth is the man who feels it incumbent upon him always to be _____facetious_____ and to turn everything into a joke. —*Fiske*

2. Our vacation became more enjoyable when we decided to take a(n) _____circuitous_____ rural road instead of the interstate highway.

3. _____Lugubrious_____ cries went up continually from the professional mourners who preceded the funeral bier to the cemetery.

4. Always _____taciturn_____, he now hardly spoke at all. —*Cloete*

5. The rainbow, with its _____variegated_____ colors, is caused by the refraction and reflection of light when it strikes raindrops.

6. Into this jungle of _____abstruse_____ learning Pico plunged with all the ardor of his powerful intellect. —*Symonds*

7. Because the weather had been excellent for gardening, we reaped a(n) _____copious_____ crop of tomatoes.

8. Before beginning surgery, a surgeon spends eight to ten minutes in the _____scrupulous_____ scrubbing of his hands and forearms to prevent germs from getting into his patient's incision.

9. Faith is not at all a(n) _____nebulous_____ thing when it is based on the infallible Word of God.

10. His _____derogatory_____ comments about the meal did not endear him to the hostess.

11. Her _____fatuous_____ remarks caused her classmates to dub her an "airhead."

12. When Mordecai heard of the _____nefarious_____ plot to assassinate King Ahasuerus, he informed Esther, who in turn warned the king.

EXERCISE B *For each word in column* **A,** *select a word from column* **B** *that is most nearly an* **antonym** *of that word. Write its letter in the blank provided.*

	A		B
e	1. copious	a.	forthright
i	2. scrupulous	b.	sensible
g	3. nebulous	c.	deep
j	4. facetious	d.	joyous
k	5. taciturn	e.	meager
b	6. fatuous	f.	winding
n	7. abstruse	g.	lucid
d	8. lugubrious	h.	approbatory
l	9. nefarious	i.	neglectful
h	10. derogatory	j.	grave
m	11. variegated	k.	garrulous
a	12. circuitous	l.	virtuous
		m.	unvaried
		n.	intelligible

EXERCISE C *Word Analysis.*

1. *Learn the meanings of the following word parts.*

Prefixes:	Roots:	Suffixes:
ab- (a-, abs-) away (from), from	AUTO self	**-ite** one who; pertaining to, having the quality of
contra-, contro- against, opposite	CLAM, CLAIM to cry out	**-ity** state, quality, act of
inter- between, among	EQU equal, even	**-tude** state, quality, act of
peri- around	FUND, FUS, FOUND to pour, to melt	**-ure** state, quality, act, result of
	GRAPH, GRAM to write	
	LOG, LOGUE speech, word, reasoning	
	PHYSI nature	
	TEND, TENS, TENT to stretch, to strive	
	VID, VIS to see	

2. *Using the Word Analyzer, write down the literal meaning of the following words. First, write the meanings of the various parts; next, rearrange the wording of the parts to formulate a good definition.*

supervision	super-	PREFIX	=	over, above, beyond
	VIS	ROOT	=	to see
	-ion	SUFFIX	=	state, quality, act of, -ing
		DEFINITION	=	overseeing
uncontradictory	un-	PREFIX	=	not
	contra-	PREFIX	=	against, opposite
	DICT	ROOT	=	to say
	-ory[1]	SUFFIX	=	like, pertaining to
		DEFINITION	=	pertaining to not saying opposite
infusibility	in-[1]	PREFIX	=	in, into
	FUS	ROOT	=	to pour, to melt
	-ibil (-ible)	SUFFIX	=	able to be
	-ity	SUFFIX	=	state, quality, act of
		DEFINITION	=	quality of being able to be poured into

Unit 11

EXERCISE D *Verbal Analogies. In each of the following questions, a related pair of words phrases is followed by five lettered pairs of words or phrases. Select the pair that best expresses a relationship similar to that expressed in the original pair. Circle the letter of your answer. [How to understand analogies is explained on pages viii–x.]*

1. TOWEL : DRY ::
 (a) chalk : board
 (b) refrigerator : electricity
 (c) drawing : color
 (d) pen : write
 (e) staples : stapler

2. DISSATISFACTION : STRIKE ::
 (a) fire : wood
 (b) protasis : drama
 (c) tadpole : frog
 (d) preface : book
 (e) contention : war

3. FACETIOUSLY : JOCULAR ::
 (a) tortuous : circuitously
 (b) abstrusely : exiguous
 (c) derogatorily : depreciatory
 (d) scrupulousness : principled
 (e) nebulous : muddled

1. A *towel* is used to *dry* as a *pen* is used to *write*.
2. *Dissatisfaction* leads to a *strike*; *contention* leads to *war*. Both indicate conflict.
3. *Facetiously* is an adverb that is related to the adjective *jocular*; *derogatorily* is an adverb that is related to the adjective *depreciatory*. *Circuitously* is an adverb that is related to the adjective *tortuous*, but these words are not in the same order as the question pair.

83

EXERCISE E *Write an original sentence with each of the following words.* Answers will vary.

1. circuitous _____

_____

_____

2. derogatory _____

_____

_____

3. facetious _____

_____

_____

4. lugubrious _____

_____

_____

5. taciturn _____

_____

_____

Everyday Expressions

Dead As a Doornail

The expression, "dead as a doornail," is one of the most common folk-sayings in the English language, in all ranks of society, probably—and that is all the more remarkable because the doornail to which it refers is obsolete save in some very old-fashioned houses, or houses that are built to imitate the old-fashioned.

Before doorbells of the wire-pull variety, or the later push-button electric sort, came into general use, the usual method of announcement of a visit was by means of pounding with a door knocker. The visitor raised the knocker and struck it against a metal plate set into a panel of the door.

This plate was fastened sometimes by a doornail, and as it was constantly being pounded on the head, it was assumed that the life was hammered out of it very soon.

From this fact it was further assumed that nothing could possibly be deader than a doorknob or doornail. Hence the expression, "as dead as a doornail."

UNIT 12

Precocious (Word History)

The Latin word *praecox* meaning "ripe before its time" came from the Latin word *praecoquere* meaning "to cook beforehand" (*prae-* before + *coquere* to cook). The word came into English as *precocious*. It was first applied to trees and plants to mean "flowering or fruiting early or before the usual time." Then the usage of *precocious* was expanded to refer to people, with the meaning "prematurely developed in some faculty."

Wolfgang Mozart, regarded by many as the greatest musical genius of all time, illustrates very well the meaning of the word *precocious*. Mozart's musical talent was obvious by the time he was three years of age. By the age of four he had learned to play the harpsichord, and by age five had begun composing his own music. By the time he was fourteen, he had already composed many sonatas, some orchestral pieces, and other works. Before his untimely death at nearly thirty-six, he had composed over six hundred works. Could we not say that Mozart was "really cooking" before the usual time?

PRE-TEST *In each group below, circle the letter of the word that is nearest in meaning to the word at the left. Then check your answers to see how you rate.*

1. **bellicose** (a) indulgent (b) temperate (c) warlike (d) furtive
2. **demur** (a) acquit (b) delay (c) scourge (d) accede
3. **mollify** (a) exasperate (b) applaud (c) appease (d) extol
4. **abstemious** (a) inadvertent (b) temperate (c) peaceable (d) deliberate
5. **opprobrious** (a) reproachful (b) belligerent (c) pugnacious (d) commendatory
6. **desultory** (a) friendly (b) industrious (c) indolent (d) unmethodical
7. **pernicious** (a) combative (b) destructive (c) disgraceful (d) amicable
8. **assiduous** (a) diligent (b) brilliant (c) backward (d) abstinent
9. **precocious** (a) pugnacious (b) sedulous (c) advanced (d) indolent
10. **castigate** (a) chastise (b) aggravate (c) exculpate (d) mitigate
11. **fortuitous** (a) methodical (b) industrious (c) unsystematic (d) accidental
12. **covert** (a) apparent (b) random (c) orderly (d) hidden

NUMBER CORRECT [ ] **RATING** ☐ Extraordinary ☐ Excellent ☐ Good
11–12 correct   9–10 correct   7–8 correct

Unit
12

1. abstemious	4. castigate	7. desultory	10. opprobrious
2. assiduous	5. covert	8. fortuitous	11. pernicious
3. bellicose	6. demur	9. mollify	12. precocious

1. ab•ste′mi•ous (ăb•stē′mĭ•us), *adj.* [From Latin *abstemius: ab- (abs-)* away from + *temetum* intoxicating drink.]

> ### *Moderate in eating and drinking; characterized by abstinence.*
>
> The physician warned his obese patient that only an *abstemious* diet would increase his chances of surviving another heart attack.

Synonyms: temperate, abstinent, sober, continent
Antonyms: gluttonous, insatiate, indulgent, intemperate
Related forms: abstemiously (adv.), abstemiousness (n.)

2. as•sid′u•ous (a•sĭd′ŭ•us), *adj.* [From Latin *assiduus,* from *assidere: ad- (as-)* to, toward + *sidere* to sit.]

> ### *Constant in application to the work at hand, diligent; unremitting, persistent*
>
> Ecclesiastes 9:10 exhorts us to be *assiduous:* "Whatsoever thy hand findeth to do, do it with thy might."

Synonyms: industrious, sedulous, indefatigable, unflagging
Antonyms: desultory, slothful, indolent
Related forms: assiduously (adv.), assiduousness (n.), assiduity (n.)

3. bel′li•cose (bĕl′ĭ•kōs), *adj.* [From Latin *bellicosus* warlike, from *bellicus* pertaining to war, from *bellum* war.]

> ### *Inclined to fighting; warlike.*
>
> In Greek mythology, the Amazons are *bellicose* women who possess phenomenal strength.

Synonyms: hostile, belligerent, pugnacious, combative
Antonyms: pacific, amicable, peaceable, friendly
Related forms: bellicosely (adv.), bellicosity (n.)

4. cas′ti•gate (kăs′ti•gāt), *v.* [From Latin *castigare* to induce to moral purity: *castus* clean, morally pure + *agere* to drive, to lead.]

> ### *To punish or rebuke severely.*
>
> By refusing to see him for five years, David roundly *castigated* Absalom for murdering Amnon.

Synonyms: chastise, chasten, scourge, berate, upbraid, censure
Antonyms: pardon, acquit, exculpate, praise, extol, applaud
Related forms: castigation (n.), castigator (n.), castigatory (adj.)

5. cov′ert (kŭv′ĕrt) [From Old French *covrir,* from Latin *cooperire* to cover completely: *co-* thoroughly + *operire* to hide, to cover.]

> *adj.* ### *Concealed, hidden, secret, disguised.*
>
> General Parker planned a *covert* mission to rescue the captive soldiers after dark.

Synonyms: clandestine, surreptitious, furtive, underhanded
Antonyms: overt, unconcealed, manifest, apparent

> *n.* ### *A covering; a shelter or hiding place.*
>
> "There shall be a tabernacle for a shadow in the daytime from the heat, and for a place of refuge, and for a *covert* from storm and from rain." —Isaiah 4:6

Synonyms: refuge, harbor, haven, sanctuary
Antonyms: exposure
Related forms: covertly (adv.), covertness (n.)

6. de•mur′ (dē•mûr′), *v.* [From Latin *demorari* to linger, delay: *de-* thoroughly + *morari* to delay.]

> ### *To delay because of doubts or obligations; to take exception to.*
>
> The spokesman for the agency *demurred* at the impertinent questions of the obnoxious reporters.

Synonyms: scruple, balk, hesitate; object, protest, dissent
Antonyms: accede, forward, promote; acquiesce, assent, concur
Related form: demur (n.)

7. **des′ul•to′ry** (dĕs′*ul*•tō′rĭ), *adj.* [From Latin *desultorius* belonging to a leaper, from *desultor* leaper (used of a performer in the Roman circus who leaped from one horse to another), from *de-* down + *salire* to leap, jump.]

> ***Jumping from one thing to another in a haphazard way; unmethodical.***
>
> *Desultory* reading is indeed very mischievous, by fostering habits of loose, discontinuous thought. —*Hare*
>
> *Synonyms:* casual, haphazard, random, orderless, unsystematic
> *Antonyms:* methodical, systematic, orderly, businesslike
> *Related forms:* desultorily (adv.), desultoriness (n.), desultorious (adj.)

8. **for•tu′i•tous** (fôr•tū′*i*•t*us*), *adj.* [From Latin *fortuitus,* from *forte* by chance.]

> ***Happening by chance or accident.***
>
> The universe did not begin by a *fortuitous* blending of gases and particles, but rather by the direct creation of Almighty God.
>
> *Synonyms:* accidental, unplanned, inadvertent, unintentional
> *Antonyms:* designed, planned, devised, deliberate
> *Related forms:* fortuitously (adv.), fortuitousness (n.), fortuity (n.)

9. **mol′li•fy** (mŏl′*i*•fī), *v.* [From Latin *mollificare: mollis* soft + *facere* to make.]

> ***To soften the anger of or to soothe hurt feelings; to make less intense or severe.***
>
> Faithful preachers of God's Word do not *mollify* the plain statements of Scripture in order to curry favor with their hearers.
>
> *Synonyms:* appease, placate, pacify; abate, alleviate, mitigate
> *Antonyms:* anger, exasperate, provoke; aggravate, intensify, worsen
> *Related forms:* mollifying (adj.), mollification (n.), mollifiable (adj.), mollifier (n.)

10. **op•pro′bri•ous** (o•prō′brĭ•*us*), *adj.* [From Latin *opprobrium: ob-* against + *probrum* reproach.]

> ***Attaching shame or disgrace; bringing reproach.***
>
> The multitude pressed round the king's coach, and insulted him with *opprobrious* cries. —*Macaulay*
>
> *Synonyms:* reproachful, disgraceful, abusive, insulting, offensive, contumelious
> *Antonyms:* commendatory, laudatory, complimentary
> *Related forms:* opprobriously (adv.), opprobriousness (n.), opprobrium (n.)

11. **per•ni′cious** (pĕr•nĭsh′*us*), *adj.* [From Latin *perniciosus,* from *pernicies* destruction: *per-* thoroughly + *necare* to kill.]

> ***Very destructive.***
>
> "There shall be false teachers among you, who privily shall bring in damnable heresies, . . . and many shall follow their *pernicious* ways." —*2 Peter 2:1–2*
>
> *Synonyms:* baneful, noxious, deleterious, detrimental, ruinous, injurious
> *Antonyms:* innocuous, harmless, uncorrupting, innocent
> *Related forms:* perniciously (adv.), perniciousness (n.)

12. **pre•co′cious** (prĕ•kō′sh*us*), *adj.* [From Latin *praecox* premature, from *praecoquere* to cook beforehand: *pre- (prae-)* before + *coquere* to boil, cook, ripen.]

> ***Developed or matured before the usual time (refers especially to mental aptitude).***
>
> The vocabulary used by the *precocious* four-year-old amazed everyone.
>
> *Synonyms:* advanced, brilliant, premature
> *Antonyms:* backward, underdeveloped, retarded
> *Related forms:* precociously (adv.), precociousness (n.), precocity (n.)

EXERCISE A *From the list of vocabulary words in this unit, choose the one that best completes each of the following sentences. Write the word in the blank provided.*

1. The governor was dumbfounded by the ___opprobrious___ accusations of the investigative commission.
2. Because the injudicious mother always tried to ___mollify___ her peevish son by giving him cookies and candy, he soon became quite plump.
3. A(n) ___abstemious___ gentleman, Benjamin Franklin thought that "three good meals a day is bad living."
4. Attila the Hun, a(n) ___bellicose___ king of the barbarous Mongols, invaded and plundered Europe during the fifth century.
5. The same ___assiduous___ cultivation was bestowed . . . to improve the minds of the sons and nephews of Constantine. *—Edward Gibbon*
6. Yet he read a great deal in a(n) ___desultory___ manner, without any scheme of study, as chance threw books in his way and inclination directed him through them. *—James Boswell*
7. The Puritan elders decided to ___castigate___ the guilty man by having him spend a day in the stocks.
8. Because she had a previous obligation, Jessica ___demurred___ at the invitation to dinner.
9. The hikers, caught in a thunderstorm, happened upon a cave, which provided a much appreciated ___covert___ from the wind and rain.
10. Wolfgang Mozart, a(n) ___precocious___ child, began composing minuets at the age of five.
11. Multiple sclerosis is a(n) ___pernicious___ disease which attacks the brain and spinal cord.
12. Some evolutionists foolishly believe that mankind had a(n) ___fortuitous___ beginning as a one-celled organism.

EXERCISE B *For each word in column* **A,** *select a word from column* **B** *that is most nearly an* **antonym** *of that word. Write its letter in the blank provided.*

	A	B
k		
d	**1.** mollify	**a.** slothful
b	**2.** pernicious	**b.** designed
j	**3.** fortuitous	**c.** pardon
e	**4.** bellicose	**d.** innocuous
n	**5.** covert	**e.** exposure
a	**6.** opprobrious	**f.** gluttonous
i	**7.** assiduous	**g.** insulting
m	**8.** precocious	**h.** systematic
h	**9.** demur	**i.** underdeveloped
c	**10.** desultory	**j.** pacific
f	**11.** castigate	**k.** intensify
______	**12.** abstemious	**l.** amicable
		m. assent
		n. laudatory

Unit 12

EXERCISE C *Word Analysis.*

1. *Learn the meanings of the following word parts.*

Prefixes:

ad- (a-, ac-, af-, etc.) to, toward

anti- (ant-) against, opposite

bene- good, well

dia- (di-) through, between, across, thoroughly

Roots:

CRED, CREDIT to believe, to trust

CRYPT, CRYPH, KRYPT hidden, secret

HOMO same

MAL(E) bad, evil

PLIC, PLICIT, PLEX, PLY to fold, to interweave, to tangle

QUIR, QUISIT, QUEST to ask, to seek

SAL, SIL, SULT to leap

SED, SESS, SID to sit, to settle

STRING, STRICT, STRAIN to draw tight

Suffixes:

-fy to do, to make, etc.

-ize, -ise to make, to act, to subject to

-logy, -ology discourse, study

-ty state, quality, act of

2. *Using the Word Analyzer, write down the literal meaning of the following words. First, write the meanings of the various parts; next, rearrange the wording of the parts to formulate a good definition.*

beneficial	bene-	PREFIX	=	good, well
	FIC	ROOT	=	to do, to make
	-(i)al	SUFFIX	=	like, pertaining to
		DEFINITION	=	pertaining to doing good (or making well)
cryptology	CRYPT	ROOT	=	hidden, secret
	-ology	SUFFIX	=	discourse, study
		DEFINITION	=	study of secrets
constriction	com- (con-)	PREFIX	=	with, together
	STRICT	ROOT	=	to draw tight
	-ion	SUFFIX	=	state, quality, act of, -ing
		DEFINITION	=	act of drawing tight(ly) together

EXERCISE D

Look up the word punish *in* Webster's New Dictionary of Synonyms. *Under that word you will find discriminating explanations for the following words:* chastise, castigate, *and* chasten. *After studying these words, decide which of the three words best completes each of the following sentences.*

Unit 12

1. During the American Revolution, Thomas Paine wrote pamphlets entitled *The Crisis* to

   _____castigate_____ those men who would "shrink from the service of their country in a time of crisis."

2. The Lord often _____chastens_____ Christians so that they may bring forth "the peaceable fruit of righteousness."

3. According to the Scriptures, a good father will _____chastise_____ his children if they deliberately disobey.

89

EXERCISE E *Write an original sentence with each of the following words.* **Answers will vary.**

1. assiduous _____

_____

_____

2. bellicose _____

_____

_____

3. desultory _____

_____

_____

4. fortuitous _____

_____

_____

5. mollify _____

_____

_____

Everyday Expressions

Turncoat

A "turncoat" is a traitor, a person upon whom no reliance can be placed. He turns, or changes his coat according to his interest, not according to principle.

It is believed that we get the expression "turncoat" from an early duke of Savoy, Emanuel by name. Savoy, which belongs now to Italy, was formerly a "bone of contention" between that country and France, as it lies on the border between the two countries. Emanuel had his territory raided by the forces of the two neighboring kings, and was obliged to "look sharp" to protect his interests. Sometimes he had to pretend to be French, sometimes Italian. He therefore had a coat made that was blue on one side and white on the other, and might be worn with either side out. When he was supposedly on the side of Italy he wore the blue side out, but when he had to pretend to be French he displayed the white side. He therefore became known as "Emanuel

the Turncoat," and the name has therefore come to be applied to those who turn their opinions around to suit their interests.

VOCABULARY REVIEW 4
(Units 7–12)

EXERCISE A *In each group below, circle the letter of the word that is most nearly a* **synonym** *of the word at the left.*

1. **querulous**   (a) unflagging   (b) fretful   (c) courageous   (d) contrary
2. **bucolic**   (a) artificial   (b) worthless   (c) rustic   (d) pugnacious
3. **abstruse**   (a) abstract   (b) obvious   (c) sinuous   (d) plentiful
4. **facetious**   (a) intemperate   (b) humorous   (c) devious   (d) straightforward
5. **abstemious**   (a) continent   (b) industrious   (c) insatiate   (d) belligerent
6. **covert**   (a) choleric   (b) disgraceful   (c) noxious   (d) clandestine
7. **baneful**   (a) dishonest   (b) lavish   (c) oily   (d) toxic
8. **mollify**   (a) pacify   (b) protest   (c) concur   (d) provoke
9. **histrionic**   (a) salutary   (b) argumentative   (c) theatrical   (d) pastoral
10. **destitute**   (a) shrewd   (b) craven   (c) genuine   (d) needy
11. **circuitous**   (a) winding   (b) furtive   (c) disinclined   (d) ostensible
12. **bellicose**   (a) slothful   (b) hostile   (c) gluttonous   (d) amicable
13. **demur**   (a) acquit   (b) appease   (c) balk   (d) berate
14. **dilettante**   (a) connoisseur   (b) pettifogger   (c) nonprofessional   (d) recluse
15. **opprobrious**   (a) commendatory   (b) harmless   (c) underdeveloped   (d) disgraceful
16. **nebulous**   (a) accidental   (b) melancholy   (c) upright   (d) obscure
17. **nefarious**   (a) joyous   (b) corrupt   (c) sensible   (d) moral
18. **puerile**   (a) contumelious   (b) nightly   (c) heavenly   (d) immature
19. **intrinsic**   (a) inborn   (b) foreign   (c) expiring   (d) dramatic
20. **acrimonious**   (a) ruinous   (b) prevaricating   (c) caustic   (d) miserly

EXERCISE B *In each group below, circle the letter of the word that is most nearly an* **antonym** *of the word at the left.*

1. **salubrious**   (a) recondite   (b) detrimental   (c) agreeable   (d) pejorative
2. **lucrative**   (a) devious   (b) worldly   (c) childish   (d) unprofitable
3. **sanguine**   (a) rosy-cheeked   (b) pessimistic   (c) mature   (d) celestial
4. **fatuous**   (a) waggish   (b) doleful   (c) villainous   (d) prudent
5. **fulsome**   (a) admirable   (b) healthful   (c) colorless   (d) light-hearted
6. **opprobrious**   (a) meticulous   (b) innocent   (c) complimentary   (d) backward
7. **bucolic**   (a) melodramatic   (b) cultured   (c) ingrained   (d) dappled
8. **intrinsic**   (a) innate   (b) expiring   (c) rhetorical   (d) extraneous
9. **mendacious**   (a) gracious   (b) sanitary   (c) scrupulous   (d) untruthful
10. **scrupulous**   (a) inadvertent   (b) righteous   (c) unprincipled   (d) cheerful
11. **demur**   (a) hesitate   (b) placate   (c) promote   (d) anger
12. **assiduous**   (a) indolent   (b) temperate   (c) hostile   (d) combative
13. **circuitous**   (a) detracting   (b) direct   (c) deep   (d) deliberate
14. **histrionic**   (a) natural   (b) theatrical   (c) rural   (d) refined
15. **loquacious**   (a) haphazard   (b) eager   (c) taciturn   (d) praiseworthy

Units
7–12

91

EXERCISE C *In each group below, circle the letter of the word that is nearest in meaning to the expression in* **boldface type.**

1. so **opposed** to accepting suggestions that he became a liability to the company
    (a) abstruse   (b) averse   (c) taciturn   (d) bellicose

2. replete with **morally harmful** teachings
    (a) incipient   (b) derogatory   (c) noxious   (d) assiduous

3. so **habitually silent** that he seldom uttered a complete sentence
    (a) taciturn   (b) abstemious   (c) puerile   (d) mundane

4. could not penetrate the **difficult to understand** wording of the insurance contract
    (a) specious   (b) abstruse   (c) circuitous   (d) opprobrious

5. the rockslide which **made impossible** travel on the mountain road
    (a) demurred   (b) derogated   (c) mollified   (d) precluded

6. because the information had definite **formal argumentation** value
    (a) histrionic   (b) loquacious   (c) forensic   (d) desultory

7. the Auca Indians, a **warlike** tribe
    (a) nefarious   (b) pernicious   (c) bellicose   (d) baneful

8. became a nuisance because of his **clumsy, joking** remarks
    (a) derogatory   (b) mundane   (c) facetious   (d) unctuous

9. a story with too much of a **tearfully sentimental** element in it
    (a) sanguine   (b) fatuous   (c) nocturnal   (d) maudlin

10. a **worldly** drama that portrayed a social ill
    (a) bucolic   (b) querulous   (c) volatile   (d) secular

11. **unmethodical** work which proved too costly and time consuming
    (a) circuitous   (b) desultory   (c) copious   (d) sedulous

12. admired his **unremitting, persistent** struggle against the weeds in his lawn
    (a) scrupulous   (b) assiduous   (c) precocious   (d) surreptitious

13. noted for his **very exact** observance of the finer points of ceremony
    (a) sedulous   (b) fortuitous   (c) punctilious   (d) assiduous

14. shared their **plentiful** harvest with others
    (a) precocious   (b) copious   (c) propitious   (d) lucrative

15. wisely rejected the **very destructive** teaching that there are no absolutes
    (a) pernicious   (b) culpable   (c) specious   (d) nefarious

16. was **punished or rebuked severely** for his egregious error in selecting materials for the roadway
    (a) mollified   (b) castigated   (c) calumniated   (d) harangued

17. happily lived in **country life** isolation
    (a) salubrious   (b) sanguine   (c) bucolic   (d) nocturnal

18. the bloodhound, noted for his sagging jowls and **mournful** expression
    (a) pusillanimous   (b) bellicose   (c) pernicious   (d) lugubrious

19. gave **childishly foolish** answers to the questions
    (a) facetious   (b) precocious   (c) derogatory   (d) puerile

20. difficult to time purchases and sales in a **changing unpredictably** stock market
    (a) nebulous   (b) variegated   (c) volatile   (d) circuitous

EXERCISE D *From the following list of vocabulary words, choose the one that best completes each of the following sentences. Write the word in the blank provided.*

castigate	derogatory	mollify	noxious	sanguine
circuitous	fulsome	nebulous	opprobrious	variegated
circumspect	incipient	nocturnal	precocious	volatile

1. Even Tutchin, acrimonious as was his nature and great as were his wrongs, seems to have been a little _____mollified_____ by the pitiable spectacle. —*Macaulay*

2. The _____precocious_____ youngster was reading literary classics by the time he was three years old.

3. The Tasmanian devil, a(n) _____nocturnal_____ animal, hides in its burrow during the day and comes out to hunt at night.

4. The _____incipient_____ rebellion should have been stopped before it turned into a full-fledged revolution.

5. At the time of the Salem witch trials, suspected witches were _____castigated_____ and persecuted throughout Connecticut, Massachusetts, and Virginia.

6. The most highly valued ruby is of a(n) _____sanguine_____ color known as pigeon blood.

7. The many sandbars forced the canoers to take a rather _____circuitous_____ route down the river.

8. The _____nebulous_____ answers given by the candidate made it evident to the people that he was not willing to commit himself to any specific goals.

9. Many men believed that his conduct in battle was _____derogatory_____ to his title as knight.

10. The Navajo Indians learned from the Pueblo Indians the colorful art of weaving _____variegated_____ blankets.

11. The Greeks probably wished that they had been more _____circumspect_____ before deciding to accept the Trojan horse from their enemy.

12. They were puffed up with the _____fulsome_____ flatteries of their philosophers and sophists. —*Bentley*

13. The _____noxious_____ fallacies of behaviorist psychology have been blithely accepted as true by many credulous educators.

Units 7–12

14. The reproachful words of the enemies of God are but the echo of the _____opprobrious_____ deeds of his unfaithful servants. —*Posey*

15. Because they cannot logically predict a woman's actions, men say that women are _____volatile_____ creatures by nature.

EXERCISE E *In each of the following analogies, a related pair of words or phrases is followed by five lettered pairs of words or phrases. Select the pair that best expresses a relationship similar to that expressed in the original pair. Circle the letter of your answer.*

1. SANGUINELY : CONFIDENT ::
    (a) puerilely : puerile
    (b) volatility : explosive
    (c) secular : secularly
    (d) forensically : forensics
    (e) histrionism : dramatic

    (adv : adj; rel.)

2. ASSIDUOUS : SEDULOUS ::
    (a) bellicose : amicable
    (b) berate : extol
    (c) abstemious : insatiate
    (d) castigate : scourge
    (e) covert : exposure

    (adj : adj; syn. / v : v; syn.)

3. PRECOCITY : BRILLIANT ::
    (a) opprobrium : opprobrious
    (b) desultorily : orderless
    (c) mollification : mollify
    (d) assiduous : assiduity
    (e) bellicosity : bellicosely

    (n : adj; rel.)

4. SENSIBLE : FATUOUS ::
    (a) nefarious : corrupt
    (b) taciturn : effusive
    (c) lugubriously : rueful
    (d) uniform : unvariegated
    (e) circuitous : circuity

    (adj : adj; ant.)

5. DEMUR : PROMOTE ::
    (a) harbor : sanctuary
    (b) desultory : casual
    (c) mollify : pacify
    (d) abusive : opprobrious
    (e) mendacious : veracious

    (v : v; ant. / adj : adj; ant.)

6. BUCOLIC : RURAL ::
    (a) histrionic : natural
    (b) puerile : adult
    (c) mundanely : earthly
    (d) intrinsic : innate
    (e) sanguine : pale

    (adj : adj; syn.)

EXERCISE F *Match each prefix, root, or suffix in column **A** with its definition in column **B**. Some definitions may be used more than once.*

	A		B
s	1. intro-, intra-	a.	one who, that which, -ing
c	2. -mony	b.	to believe, to trust
r	3. FUND, FUS, FOUND	c.	state, quality, result of
z	4. inter-	d.	to live
k	5. GRAT	e.	discourse, study
p	6. AUTO	f.	around
u	7. bene-	g.	bad, evil
b	8. CRED, CREDIT	h.	having the quality of
h	9. -ous, -ose	i.	to leap
q	10. en-	j.	to use
v	11. PHYSI	k.	free, pleasing, grateful
e	12. -logy, -ology	l.	like, pertaining to
x	13. VOC, VOK	m.	to see
w	14. contra-, contro-	n.	along with, after, beyond, change
t	15. -fy	o.	before
a	16. -ant	p.	self
m	17. VID, VIS	q.	in, into, causative
w	18. anti-	r.	to pour, to melt
j	19. US, UT	s.	inside, within
y	20. CIDE, CIS	t.	to do, to make, etc.
l	21. -al, -an¹, -ane	u.	good, well
n	22. meta-	v.	nature
g	23. MAL(E)	w.	against, opposite
f	24. circum-	x.	voice, to call
i	25. SAL, SIL, SULT	y.	to kill, to cut
		z.	between, among

Units
7–12

94

EXERCISE G *Word Analysis. The following words contain prefixes, roots, and suffixes that you have memorized. Write down from memory the literal meaning of these words. First, write the meanings of the various parts; next, rearrange the wording of the parts to formulate a good definition.*

vocal	VOC	ROOT	=	voice, to call
	-al	SUFFIX	=	like, pertaining to
		DEFINITION	=	pertaining to the voice
gratitude	GRAT(I)	ROOT	=	free, pleasing, grateful
	-tude	SUFFIX	=	state, quality, act of
		DEFINITION	=	state of being grateful
neographic	NEO	ROOT	=	new
	GRAPH	ROOT	=	to write
	-ic	SUFFIX	=	like, pertaining to
		DEFINITION	=	pertaining to new writing
homophonous	HOMO	ROOT	=	same
	PHON	ROOT	=	sound, voice
	-ous	SUFFIX	=	having the quality of
		DEFINITION	=	having the quality of the same sound
metalogical	meta-	PREFIX	=	along with, after, beyond, change
	LOG	ROOT	=	speech, word, reasoning
	-ical	SUFFIX	=	like, pertaining to
		DEFINITION	=	pertaining to beyond reasoning

Everyday Expressions

Boycott

The word *boycott*, which is in common, everyday use, is a true "figure of speech," since it is based on a proper name. The origin of its figurative use was as follows:

A certain Captain Boycott was employed as an "agent" by an absentee Irish landlord. He was oppressive and overbearing in his dealings with the tenants, and they asked the landlord to appoint another agent. He refused, and they in turn refused to have any dealings with Boycott; in fact, they extended the "boycott," or policy of non-intercourse, to anyone who communicated in any way with the hated agent. If a man accepted work from Boycott, his friends and neighbors treated him as an absolute stranger; no one was to buy from or sell to him; no one was to enter his house; no one was to recognize him in any way. The plan "worked" well; and since that time the word *boycott*, used as either a noun or a verb, has been a part of the English language.

95

Death, Be Not Proud

John Donne

Death, be not proud, though some have called thee
Mighty and dreadful, for thou art not so:
For those whom thou think'st thou dost overthrow
Die not, poor Death, nor yet canst thou kill me.
From rest and sleep, which but thy pictures be,
Much pleasure; then from thee much more must flow,
And soonest our best men with thee do go,
Rest of their bones, and souls' delivery.

Thou'rt slave to fate, chance, kings, and desperate men,
And dost with poison, war, and sickness dwell;
And poppy or charms can make us sleep as well
And better than thy stroke. Why swell'st thou then?
One short sleep past, we wake eternally
And death shall be no more: Death, thou shalt die.

On His Blindness

John Milton

When I consider how my light is spent,
Ere half my days, in this dark world and wide,
And that one talent which is death to hide
Lodged with me useless, though my soul more bent
To serve therewith my Maker, and present
My true account, lest he returning chide;
"Doth God exact day-labor, light denied?"
I fondly ask. But Patience, to prevent
That murmur, soon replies, "God doth not need
Either man's work or his own gifts; who best
Bear his mild yoke, they serve him best. His state
Is kingly: thousands at his bidding speed,
And post o'er land and ocean without rest;
They also serve who only stand and wait."

Flower in the Crannied Wall

Alfred, Lord Tennyson

Flower in the crannied wall,
I pluck you out of the crannies,
I hold you here, root and all, in my hand,
Little flower—but if I could understand
What you are, root and all, and all in all,
I should know what God and man is.

Apostrophe to the Ocean

Lord Byron

Roll on, thou deep and dark blue Ocean—roll!
Ten thousand fleets sweep over thee in vain;
Man marks the earth with ruin—his control
Stops with the shore—upon the watery plain
The wrecks are all thy deed, nor doth remain
A shadow of man's ravage, save his own,
When for a moment, like a drop of rain,
He sinks into thy depths with bubbling groan—
Without a grave, unknelled, uncoffined, and unknown.

Poetry

The World Is Too Much with Us

William Wordsworth

The world is too much with us; late and soon,
Getting and spending, we lay waste our powers;
Little we see in Nature that is ours;
We have given our hearts away, a sordid boon!
This sea that bares her bosom to the moon;
The winds that will be howling at all hours,
And are upgathered now like sleeping flowers;
For this, for everything, we are out of tune;
It moves us not. —Great God! I'd rather be
A Pagan suckled in a creed outworn;
So might I, standing on this pleasant lea,
Have glimpses that would make me less forlorn;
Have sight of Proteus rising from the sea;
Or hear old Triton blow his wreathéd horn.

Why He Was Promoted

Author Unknown

He was always on time.
He did not watch the clock.
He put his heart in his work.
He was not always grumbling.
He learned from his blunders.
> He acted on his own judgment.
> He was ready for the next step.
> He did not ask too many questions.
> He thought it was worth while to learn how.
> He chose his friends among his superiors.
>> He did not ruin his ability by half doing things.
>> He imitated the habits of men who could
>>> accomplish more than he could.
>> He learned that the best part of his salary
>>> was not in his envelope.

To Be, or Not to Be

William Shakespeare

To be, or not to be, that is the question:
Whether 'tis nobler in the mind to suffer
The slings and arrows of outrageous fortune,
Or to take arms against a sea of troubles
And by opposing end them. To die, to sleep—
No more; and by a sleep to say we end
The heartache, and the thousand natural shocks
That flesh is heir to. 'Tis a consummation
Devoutly to be wished. To die, to sleep.
To sleep—perchance to dream: ay, there's the rub!
For in that sleep of death what dreams may come
When we have shuffled off this mortal coil,
Must give us pause. There's the respect
That makes calamity of so long life.
For who would bear the whips and scorns of time,
The oppressor's wrong, the proud man's contumely,
The pangs of despised love, the law's delay,
The insolence of office, and the spurns
That patient merit of the unworthy takes,
When he himself might his quietus make
With a bare bodkin? Who would fardels bear,
To grunt and sweat under a weary life,
But that the dread of something after death,
The undiscovered country from whose bourn
No traveller returns—puzzles the will,
And makes us rather bear those ills we have
Than fly to others that we know not of?
Thus conscience does make cowards of us all,
And thus the native hue of resolution
Is sicklied o'er with the pale cast of thought,
And enterprises of great pitch and moment
With this regard their currents turn awry
And lose the name of action.

Sonnet 43

Elizabeth Barrett Browning

How do I love thee? Let me count the ways.
I love thee to the depth and breadth and height
My soul can reach, when feeling out of sight
For the ends of Being and ideal Grace.
I love thee to the level of every day's
Most quiet need, by sun and candlelight.
I love thee freely, as men strive for Right;
I love thee purely, as they turn from Praise.
I love thee with the passion put to use
In my old griefs, and with my childhood's faith.
I love thee with a love I seemed to lose
With my lost saints—I love thee with the breath,
Smiles, tears of all my life!—and, if God choose,
I shall but love thee better after death.

Dust of Snow

Robert Frost

The way a crow
Shook down on me
The dust of snow
From a hemlock tree
Has given my heart
A change of mood
And saved some part
Of a day I had rued.

Poetry

My Heart Leaps Up

William Wordsworth

My heart leaps up when I behold
   A rainbow in the sky.
So was it when my life began;
So is it now I am a man,
So be it when I shall grow old,
   Or let me die!
The child is father of the man;
And I could wish my days to be
Bound each to each by natural piety.

Index

Entries in **boldface** type are the main vocabulary words, prefixes, roots, and suffixes taught in this book. Entries in regular type are (1) synonyms or antonyms of the main vocabulary words or (2) words, prefixes, roots, and suffixes which appear only in the word-analysis exercises. *Numbers* in **boldface** type indicate the place where an entry receives its fullest treatment. Numbers in *italic* type indicate the place where a word history is given.

104

Index